PUZZLE
BOOK

RACING POST

240 PUZZLES
To Challenge the Most Committed Horse racing Fan

Alan Mortiboys

First published by Pitch Publishing on behalf of Racing Post, 2021

Pitch Publishing

A2 Yeoman Gate

Yeoman Way

Worthing

Sussex

BN13 3QZ

www.pitchpublishing.co.uk

info@pitchpublishing.co.uk

www.racingpost.com/shop

ISBN 9781839500749

Typesetting and origination by Pitch Publishing
Printed and bound in India by Replika Press Pvt. Ltd.

DEDICATION

Dedicated to my racegoing companions over the years –
(the late) Fred Mortiboys, Daniel Mortiboys
and Mary-Clarke Mortiboys.

ABOUT THE AUTHOR

Alan Mortiboys contributes questions to BBC1's *Impossible* and BBC2's *Only Connect*.

He has also been following racing since the age of nine. Encouraged by having a letter about betting systems published in the *Sporting Life Guide* when aged 14, he wrote to Peter O'Sullevan, then the racing correspondent for the BBC and the *Daily Express*, asking how to get into racing journalism. The Voice of Racing was kind enough to reply and suggested that it was a case of being in the right place at the right time. It turns out that this was not West Bromwich in the 1960s.

After a decades-long and fruitful detour working in education, Alan is finally getting the chance to build on that *Sporting Life Guide* letter and hopes these puzzles provide fun and challenges for all racing fans!

INTRODUCTION

This book has six different kinds of puzzles for racing fans. They are:

Simple Sums

A straightforward set of calculations, but do you have the racing knowledge you need to complete them?

Fill In The Blanks

Each of these puzzles gives an account of a race that has been run but with key words and names missing. Do you know enough or can you make the right guesses to fill in the blanks?

Get It In One? Or Two, Or Three, Or Four?

This gives four clues about a well-known horse, trainer or jockey. How many clues do you need to identify the well-known person or horse? One, two, three or four?

Where's The Logic?

These are traditional logic puzzles but in a racing setting. Can you use logic and the clues to solve the puzzle?

(All the names that are used in these puzzles – of horses, jockeys, trainers, stables, owners, racecourse staff, bookmakers, tipsters, punters and racecourses – are intended to be fictitious.)

Tell Me The Answer And I'll Tell You The Question

This puzzle gives you two questions and two answers but only one question and one answer make a match. Can you find the matching pair?

Time For A Rhyme

This puzzle takes the form of an incomplete poem about a horse, a trainer or a jockey. Can you complete the missing rhymes and identify the person or horse?

Good luck!

SIMPLE SUMS

1.

Begin with the number of times Frankel won the Sussex Stakes

Multiply by the number of letters in the name of the 2019 Epsom Derby winner

Add the number of times Johnny Murtagh rode the winner of the King George VI and Queen Elizabeth Stakes

Divide by the number of furlongs run in the Falmouth Stakes

What is the number you have arrived at?

Is it:

A.   The number of King George VI chases won by Desert Orchid?

B.   The number of King George VI chases won by Wayward Lad?

C.   The number of King George VI chases won by Silviniaco Conti?

2.

Begin with the number of times Red Rum ran in the Grand National

Multiply by the number of times Faugheen won the Christmas Hurdle

Add the number of times Gordon Richards was champion flat jockey

Divide by the number of letters in the name of the 2020 2,000 Guineas winner.

What is the number you have arrived at?

Is it:

A.   The age of Blue Point when he first won the King's Stand Stakes?

B.   The age of Equiano when he first won the King's Stand Stakes?

C.   The age of Sole Power when he first won the King's Stand Stakes?

FILL IN THE BLANKS

Can you fill in the ten blanks below? Each blank may be one word or the full name of a person, a horse or a race.

1.

The field for the 2016 running of the _____ at the Cheltenham Festival included the three most recent winners of the race, _____, _____ and _____. However, none of them were favourite; that was Un De Sceaux, who finished second to _____ in a famous victory. In third place was _____ who went on to win the race the following year. The winner was ridden by _____ and trained by _____. The winner had just one more race – the _____ at Sandown, winning once again from Un De Sceaux, but by the bigger margin of _____ lengths.

2.

Night of Thunder won the 2,000 Guineas in _____ by half a length from _____. This was the only race in which the runner-up was defeated – his subsequent Group One wins that season included the Irish 2,000 Guineas and the _____ at Royal Ascot. Third behind Night of Thunder was _____, who went on to win both the Epsom Derby and the _____ in June as well as the _____ at York in August. Eighth in the 2,000 Guineas was, the 2014 winner of the _____, Kingston Hill. The horse who finished tenth behind Night of Thunder, _____, won two Group Ones later in the season – the _____ at Chantilly and the _____.

GET IT IN ONE? OR TWO, OR THREE, OR FOUR?

How few clues do you need to identify each of these famous racehorses?

1.

He won his only race as a two-year-old, a maiden at Newmarket in October 2016, with a future Ascot Gold Cup winner finishing fourth.

In 2017 he became the first of his sire's progeny to win a European Group One race.

He started at odds-on in each of his four races as a four-year-old.

He became only the second horse this century to win consecutive Champion Stakes.

2.

This horse's dam won the Irish 1,000 Guineas, Nassau Stakes and Sun Chariot Stakes in 2008.

She won races for four different jockeys.

She won back-to-back Tattersalls Gold Cups and Irish Champion Stakes.

She finished second to Enable on three occasions.

WHERE'S THE LOGIC?

1.

Rawcliffe the trainer had three winners in one day, all at different courses: Armfield, Bowminster and Cornham. The horses' names were Duplicity, Euphoria and Fidelity. The jockeys were Ashton, Bradshaw and Carter.

Bradshaw rode the winner at Armfield. At Cornham, the winner was 10-1. Duplicity won at 2-1. Euphoria's win was not at Bowminster. Ashton won on the banker at 4-6.

Which horse won at Cornham?

2.

Four friends went to the races and in the first race they each backed a different horse, one of the first four in the betting. They each had a different stake and they placed their bets with four different bookmakers, Bell, Chamberlin, Chapman and Weaver.

Bell took Chris's bet which was not the £20 that was placed on the favourite. Jude backed the fourth in the betting. Chamberlin took the bet on the second favourite, which was not £50. Chapman took the £30 bet. Jamie's bet was not the £10 one.

Which horse did Alex back?

TELL ME THE ANSWER AND I'LL TELL YOU THE QUESTION

In each set of two questions and two answers below, only one of the answers is correct for only one of the questions. Can you find the matching pair?

1.

Questions

Which woman trained the Grand National winner in 2009?

Which woman trained the Grand National winner in 2013?

Answers

Sue Smith

Lucinda Russell

2.

Questions

Which race named after a monarch was first run under that name in 1937?

Which race named after a monarch was first run under that name in 1955?

Answers

King George VI Chase

Queen Anne Stakes

3.

Questions

Which runner-up in the 2,000 Guineas won the Irish 2,000 Guineas in his next race?

Which runner-up in the 2,000 Guineas won the St James's Palace Stakes in his next race?

Answers

Sir Percy

Kingman

4.

Questions

Which two-time winner of the Champion Hurdle had his second win aged eight?

Which two-time winner of the Champion Hurdle had his second win aged nine?

Answers

Comedy of Errors

Sea Pigeon

SIMPLE SUMS

3.

Begin with the number of consecutive races won by Sprinter Sacre in his winning run which began in December 2011

Add the number of letters in the name of the 2016 winner of the 2,000 Guineas

Subtract the number of letters in the name of the 2016 winner of the 1,000 Guineas

Divide by the number of times Joseph O' Brien rode the winner of the Epsom Derby

What is the number you have arrived at?

Is it:

A. The age Rooster Booster was when he won the Champion Hurdle?

B. The age Annie Power was when she won the Champion Hurdle?

C. The age Rock On Ruby was when he won the Champion Hurdle?

4.

Begin with the number of times Lester Piggott rode the winner of the St Leger

Multiply by the number of times St Nicholas Abbey won the Coronation Cup

Add the number of times John Francome was outright jump champion jockey

Divide by the number of Group One races normally run in a season at York

What is the number you have arrived at?

Is it:

A.   The number of letters in the name of the 2014 winner of the Cheltenham Gold Cup?

B.   The number of letters in the name of the 2015 winner of the Cheltenham Gold Cup?

C.   The number of letters in the name of the 2016 winner of the Cheltenham Gold Cup?

FILL IN THE BLANKS

Can you fill in the ten blanks below? Each blank may be one word, or the full name of a person, a horse or a race.

3.

The winner of the 2016 _____ was Ivanovich Gorbatov whose trainer, _____, is better known for his successes on the flat and whose son, _____, later took over the training of the horse. Second was _____ who in her next race, the Anniversary Four-year-old Novices' Hurdle at _____, reversed placings with the winner and beat him by 41 lengths in the first of what was to become her _____ Grade One successes. The third, _____, was back at the Cheltenham Festival with a win two years later in the Arkle Challenge Trophy Chase. It is unlikely that anyone would have predicted that two of the unplaced horses – who were stablemates – would go on to win three consecutive _____ between them. They were _____ in sixth and _____ in eighth.

4.

Was won the _____ at Epsom in 2012, with a starting price of _____. Trained by _____, it was a first British Classic winner for jockey _____. In six subsequent starts, the winner failed to win again. The second horse, _____, also did not subsequently win a race, although later in 2012 she was _____ in the Irish Oaks. The beaten favourite in third place at Epsom, trained by _____, was _____, who went on to great success. She won Group One races as a three, four and five-year-old. These included the _____ at Goodwood, the Yorkshire Oaks and the _____ at Royal Ascot.

GET IT IN ONE? OR TWO, OR THREE, OR FOUR?

How few clues do you need to identify each of these famous racehorses?

3.

Foaled in 1999, her dam won the 1990 Yorkshire Oaks.

She was ridden in all races by Kieren Fallon.

She won consecutive Yorkshire Oaks, on each occasion having that year's Epsom Oaks winner in rear.

She won the Breeders' Cup Filly and Mare Turf in 2003.

4.

She was ridden in her Group One wins by Jimmy Fortune and William Buick.

Her fifth foal's wins included the Prix Jean Prat and Sussex Stakes.

She was disqualified from victory in the Prix Vermeille at Longchamp.

Her final race and Group One win was the Dubai Sheema Classic.

WHERE'S THE LOGIC?

3.

The hurdler Gormenghast was having a very successful season, having won all four starts to date. Each win was at a different distance (the longest of which was two miles and six furlongs) and on different going and he started at a different price each time! They were also at four different courses, Armfield, Bowminster, Cornham and Denley. His win at Bowminster was over two miles and two furlongs. The win over two miles was in heavy going; it was not the one in which he started at evens. When he won at two and a half miles, he started at 5-2; this was not at Cornham, where the win was on good going. He started at 2-1 at Denley but he was 6-1 when he won on good to soft. Where did Gormenghast win on soft going?

4.

There are just four runners in the last race on the card. Each of the jockeys has a different colour cap from each other – red, blue, yellow and green – and different colour sleeves from each other, as well as a different pattern on the body of the colours.

The jockey on the horse drawn one has a green cap but is not the jockey wearing green sleeves with quartered colours. The jockey on the horse drawn two has red sleeves and the jockey in stall three has hooped colours. Blue sleeves are worn by the jockey with a red cap. The jockey with a diamond is not the one with yellow sleeves. The jockey with a blue cap does not have a diamond.

What colour was the cap of the jockey with red sleeves? The jockey in which stall is wearing crossbelts?

TIME FOR A RHYME

Can you complete the missing rhymes in the poems below and identify the horse that the poem is about?

1.

For many years racegoers were thrilled and beguiled

By the exploits of this offspring of _____

His starts numbered 70, his wins 34

To win a great Gold Cup, he kept pulling out _____

2.

22 hurdles races, 11 were won

Normal rider Mccoy and trained by _____

His speed over a hurdle was a sight to see

In the green with yellow hoops of owner _____

3.

He beat Florida Pearl in the King George by ten

A fifth win in the race for his trainer _____

More wins were to come in Ireland and at Aintree

In the safe hands of the trainer's son _____

4.

Perhaps the best with which Greystoke was ever graced

His sire in both the Guineas and Derby was _____

At fences he was flamboyant, fast and clever

With his Champion Chase win one of the best _____

SIMPLE SUMS

5.

Begin with the number of times Blue Point won the King's Stand Stakes

Add the number of Grade Ones won by Hurricane Fly

Multiply by the number of racecourses in Cumbria

Divide by the number of hurdles jumped in the Long Walk Hurdle

What is the number you have arrived at?

Is it:

A. The number of times Barry Geraghty rode the winner of the Champion Hurdle?

B. The number of times Tony McCoy rode the winner of the Champion Hurdle?

C. The number of times Noel Fehily rode the winner of the Champion Hurdle?

6.

Begin with the number of fences jumped in the Tingle Creek Chase

Add the age that Addeybb was when he won the 2020 Champion Stakes

Multiply by the number of times Warsaan won the Coronation Cup

Subtract the number of consecutive races won by Winx

What is the number you have arrived at?

Is it:

A. The number of times Further Flight won the Doncaster Cup?

B. The number of times Further Flight won the Goodwood Cup?

C. The number of times Further Flight won the Jockey Club Cup?

FILL IN THE BLANKS

Can you fill in the ten blanks below? Each blank may be one word, or the full name of a person, a horse, a race.

5.

The Champion Stakes in _____ was won by _____, whose full brother, _____, had won the race two years previously. Both were by Galileo out of _____. This was the winner's third Group One success that season, following victories in the _____ in Ireland and the _____ in France. He was ridden in all three wins by _____. In second place, beaten a _____, was Al Kazeem who himself was a winner of the _____ at the Curragh in 2013 and 2015. In fifth place was the horse who won the race three years before, _____.

6.

The Ryanair Chase at Cheltenham in _____ was won by _____, ridden by _____ and trained by Nigel Twiston-Davies. The winner had already won the Paddy Power Gold Cup at Cheltenham and would go on to win the 2010 _____ at the Festival. He beat the odds-on favourite, _____, by two lengths. The second had already won four Grade One Chases including both the _____ in 2006 and the _____ in 2007 at the Cheltenham Festival. Back in sixth was _____, a horse who later had the _____ at Aintree renamed after him, following his _____ wins in the race.

GET IT IN ONE? OR TWO, OR THREE, OR FOUR?

How few clues do you need to identify each of these famous trainers?

5.

Born July 1975, his first job at Newmarket, aged 16, was working for Susan Piggott.

He saddled his first Group One winner in November 2013 when Outstrip landed the Breeders' Cup Juvenile Turf at Santa Anita, USA.

His first UK Group One winner came in October 2014, when Charming Thought won the Middle Park Stakes.

He was the first British trainer to train the winner of the Melbourne Cup.

6.

He was born in Nigeria, brought up in Ireland.

He rode just over 100 winners, under both codes, in ten years in the saddle, and shared the Conditional jockeys' title in the 1988/89 season.

He saddled a first Group One winner with Wootton Bassett in the 2010 Group One Prix Jean-Luc Lagardère at Longchamp.

The horse that was probably his best won four Group Ones and broke the track record in the Queen Anne Stakes at Royal Ascot.

WHERE'S THE LOGIC?

5.

Each of the three horses in the photo finish wore a different kind of headgear.

Advance was not third. The horse in blinkers was second or third. The horse who won was Bucolic or Carapace. Advance did not wear blinkers. Carapace wore blinkers or cheekpieces. The winner had a noseband or blinkers.

Which horse wore a noseband?

6.

Following her lottery win, Mary Barton bought four horses. She bought a two-year-old, a three-year-old, a four-year-old and a five-year-old. Each was a different colour. She placed them with four different trainers, Matthews, Nolan, Osborne and Price.

The black horse was with Nolan and the four-year-old with Matthews. The grey five-year-old was not with Osborne at Thornfield Hall. The two-year-old was not a bay and not at the Manderley stables. The brown horse was at Twelve Oaks.

What colour was the horse stabled at Pemberley?

TELL ME THE ANSWER AND I'LL TELL YOU THE QUESTION

In each set of two questions and two answers below, only one of the answers is correct for only one of the questions. Can you find the matching pair?

5.

Questions

Which 21st century Epsom Derby winner was the first to be sired by Sadler's Wells?

Which 21st century Epsom Derby winner was the first to be sired by Cape Cross?

Answers

Motivator

Sea the Stars

6.

Questions

Which former racecourse closed in 1962?

Which former racecourse closed in 1970?

Answers

Alexandra Park

Manchester

7.

Questions

Which jockey's autobiography was called *A Weight Off My Mind*?
Which jockey's autobiography was called *Form*?

Answers

Barry Geraghty
Richard Hughes

8.

Questions

Who trained their first St Leger winner in 2014?
Who trained their first St Leger winner in 2015?

Answers

Laura Mongan
Ralph Beckett

SIMPLE SUMS

7.

Begin with the number of times that Cue Card won the Betfair Chase

Multiply by the number of times Richard Dunwoody was champion jumps jockey

Add the number of different fences jumped in the Grand National

Subtract the number of races won by Secretariat

What is the number you have arrived at?

Is it:

A.   The age of Arkle when he won his first Cheltenham Gold Cup?

B.   The age of Arkle when he won his second Cheltenham Gold Cup?

C.   The age of Arkle when he won his third Cheltenham Gold Cup?

8.

Begin with the number of Group Ones won by Winx

Multiply by the number of times Sprinter Sacre won the Queen Mother Champion Chase

Divide by the number of lengths by which Shergar won the Epsom Derby

Subtract the number of consecutive years that Richard Johnson was champion jump jockey starting with the 2015-16 season

What is the number you have arrived at?

Is it:

A.   The number of Group One races normally run in a season at Goodwood?

B.   The number of Group One races normally run in a season at Haydock?

C.   The number of Group One races normally run in a season at Doncaster?

FILL IN THE BLANKS

Can you fill in the ten blanks below? Each blank may be one word, or the full name of a person, a horse or a race.

7.

The _____ in _____ was won by Too Darn Hot. This was his last appearance on a racecourse and his third Group One win, following his previous race, the Prix Jean Prat at _____ and, as a two-year-old, the _____ at Newmarket. At the end of his first season, he won the Cartier Award for Champion Two-year-old Colt. At Goodwood, he beat _____ into second place, reversing his defeat by that colt in the _____ at Royal Ascot. In sixth place at Goodwood was _____, who had beaten Too Darn Hot into second place in the Irish 2,000 Guineas. Too Darn Hot was trained by John Gosden and ridden in all of his races by _____ carrying the pink with a _____ sash colours of Lord Lloyd-Webber. He started favourite or joint-favourite in each of his _____ races.

8.

The King George VI Chase in _____ was won by the _____-year-old _____. He was ridden by _____ and trained by _____ for whom this was a tenth win in the race. He won from Thistlecrack and _____, winner of that year's Cheltenham Gold Cup. Another Gold Cup winner, _____, who had won in 2015, unseated his rider. The winner's stablemate, _____, was ridden by _____ and finished fourth, whilst the favourite, _____, second in that year's Cheltenham Gold Cup, was last of the seven finishers.

27

GET IT IN ONE? OR TWO, OR THREE, OR FOUR?

How few clues do you need to identify each of these famous trainers?

7.

He was born in October 1959 and began training in 1987 using gallops that were part of an RAF target practice range.

The stable motto is 'Always Trying'.

The horse that he has described as his favourite won five Group Ones, including the 2004 1,000 Guineas.

His first 1,000 winners were accumulated in record time – 90 days quicker than previous holder Sir Henry Cecil.

8.

An established horse rider, she show-jumped at international level for the Welsh junior team and got her first job in racing with Peter Bowen.

Her first winner was Mango Catcher in a handicap chase at Chepstow on 5 April 2008; it was her only winner of the 2007-08 season.

The trainer's first winner at the Cheltenham Festival in 2012 would subsequently finish third in the Grand National the following year.

She trained Lisnagar Oscar to win the Stayers' Hurdle at 50-1.

WHERE'S THE LOGIC?

7.

The first four races on the card were over different distances – two miles, two miles and four furlongs, two miles and six furlongs and three miles. The biggest field of these four was for the novice chase. The handicap chase is immediately after the race over three miles. The two-mile four furlong race is not over hurdles. The handicap hurdle is immediately before the race over two miles. The novice hurdle is immediately before the handicap hurdle. The novice hurdle is not second or third on the card.

Which race on the card is over two miles six furlongs?

8.

The horse called Mishap had lived up to her name on her first four runs of the season. On each occasion she had been ridden by a different jockey and had failed to complete the race.

On her second outing, she either fell or was pulled up. The jockey Carter did not pull her up nor was he unseated. Dunphy took the ride immediately after or before Ashton, whilst Bradshaw or Carter was the most recent to ride her. Mishap unseated her rider immediately before or after the race in which she was brought down. One of the four riders took his turn in between Dunphy and Bradshaw. After the race in which she was pulled up, Bradshaw rode her next.

Who rode Mishap when she fell?

TIME FOR A RHYME

Can you complete the missing rhymes in the poems below and identify the trainer that the poem is about?

5.

He made the move to Newmarket as a young man

Coming from a top racing family in _____

His multiple Group One wins are there to be seen

As is his daughter who shines on the TV _____

6.

Over 2,000 winners for this baronet

In over 50 years at Heath House, _____

He won two Champion Stakes with Alborada

And the Prix de l'Abbaye and Nunthorpe with _____

7.

Two first season Group One wins was a super start

In 06, a second Middle Park with _____

A second season gave Guineas and Epsom glory

Then later a first Derby win for _____

8.

He began in 14 with a successful year

From his stables based near Marlborough in _____

A 40-1 Guineas win left punters shook

And again, four years later thanks to _____

SIMPLE SUMS

9.

Begin with the age that Master Minded was when he won his first Tingle Creek Chase

Add the number of races won by the unbeaten Ribot

Multiply by the number of racecourses in Norfolk

Divide by the number of complete furlongs run in the Queen Alexandra Stakes

What is the number you have arrived at?

Is it:

A. The age of Kingsgate Native when he won the Nunthorpe Stakes?

B. The age of Mozart when he won the Nunthorpe Stakes?

C. The age of Marsha when she won the Nunthorpe Stakes?

10.

Begin with the number of letters in the name of the 2020 St Leger winner

Multiply by the number of finishers in the 2001 Grand National

Subtract the number of Epsom Oaks winners trained by Henry Cecil

Divide by the number of times Lester Piggott was champion flat jockey

What is the number you have arrived at?

Is it:

A. The number of times Big Buck's won the Stayers' Hurdle?

B. The number of times Inglis Drever won the Stayers' Hurdle?

C. The number of times Baracouda won the Stayers' Hurdle?

FILL IN THE BLANKS

Can you fill in the ten blanks below? Each blank may be one word, or the full name of a person, a horse or a race.

9.

The Arkle Challenge Trophy Chase in _____ was won by _____, trained by _____ and ridden by _____. He started at odds of 33-1 in what was only his _____ outing over fences. His next race, the Manifesto Novices' Chase at _____ in which he finished third to Uxizandre, proved to be his last. In fourth place at Cheltenham was _____, who went on to great success in the following season, winning three Grade Ones. These were the Tingle Creek Chase at _____, the _____ at Ascot and the Queen Mother Champion Chase. In last place behind the shock winner was _____, who had won the Champion Hurdle two years previously, in 2012.

10.

_____ won the 2011 _____ by _____ lengths at odds of 20-1. She broke the course record and became only the second filly to win the race in the 21st century. In third was another filly, _____, who had completed the double of the _____ and the Irish Oaks in the previous year. Fourth was _____, who had won the _____ at Sandown and the Irish Champion Stakes earlier in the season. The winner went on to win the King George VI and Queen Elizabeth Stakes the following year, by a _____ from _____ with _____ trained St Nicholas Abbey in third.

GET IT IN ONE? OR TWO, OR THREE, OR FOUR?

How few clues do you need to identify each of these famous jockeys?

9.

He was born in County Wexford in 1972 and apprenticed to Jim Bolger.

His first Group One win was on Commander Collins in the 1998 Racing Post Trophy.

He was top Royal Ascot jockey in 2006 with six winners.

His only Classic win was on the John Gosden-trained Lucarno in the 2007 St Leger.

10.

He was born in Herefordshire in 1977 and his first pony was called Twinkle.

His first win was on Rusty Bridge, trained by his mother Sue in a hunter chase at Hereford in April 1994.

His first Cheltenham Festival win was on 40-1 shot in the Stayers' Hurdle.

His first Jump Jockey Championship came in 2016.

WHERE'S THE LOGIC?

9.

Four friends tried to forecast the finishing order in the four-horse race. They each came up with a different forecast, although they all agreed Dumbo would be fourth.

Chris thought they would finish in alphabetical order. Jude agreed with Chris's forecast of the winner but no one agreed with Chris on the runner-up. The tipster in the paper disagreed with the four friends, saying it would be Boscobel to win from Columbo with Artichoke third. In the event, they were all correct in forecasting who would finish last, but none of the four friends or the tipster gave the first three correctly. Can you?

(By the way, there were no dead-heats in either the forecast or the result.)

10.

Half of the field of ten for the novice chase fell, one at each of the first five fences.

Eliot wasn't the one to fall at the first. The horse trained by Moran and ridden by Ashton fell at the fifth fence. Wordsworth fell at the third, the one ridden by Bradshaw fell at the second. Keats, trained by North, didn't fall at the first but he did fall before Tennyson. Milton was trained by O'Sullivan; the horse ridden by Carter was trained by Parkes. The favourite was Keats, ridden by Dunphy.

Which horse was ridden by Earnshaw? Which horse was trained by Quinn?

TELL ME THE ANSWER AND I'LL TELL YOU THE QUESTION

In each set of two questions and two answers below, only one of the answers is correct for only one of the questions. Can you find the matching pair?

9.

Questions

Which two-time winner at the Cheltenham Festival had his first win there in 2010?

Which two-time winner at the Cheltenham Festival had his first win there in 2011?

Answers

Sizing Europe

Simonsig

10.

Questions

Which winner of the King George VI and Queen Elizabeth Stakes ridden by Johnny Murtagh went on to win the Irish Champion Stakes?

Which winner of the King George VI and Queen Elizabeth Stakes ridden by Johnny Murtagh went on to win the Juddmonte International?

Answers

Duke of Marmalade

Novellist

11.

Questions

What is the number of complete furlongs in the longest race traditionally run at Glorious Goodwood?

What is the number of complete furlongs in the longest race traditionally run at Chester's May Festival?

Answers

21

20

12.

Questions

Who trained their first 1,000 Guineas winner in 2004?

Who trained their first 1,000 Guineas winner in 2006?

Answers

Mark Johnston

Aidan O'Brien

SIMPLE SUMS

11.

Begin with the number of times Willie Carson rode the winner of the Epsom Derby

Multiply by the number of times Khalid Abdullah owned the winner of the Prix de l'Arc de Triomphe

Divide by the number of furlongs in the Lockinge Stakes

Add the number of Group One races normally run in a season at Epsom

What is the number you have arrived at?

Is it:

A. The number of times Kieren Fallon was champion flat jockey?

B. The number of times Pat Eddery was champion flat jockey?

C. The number of times Richard Hughes was champion flat jockey?

12.

Begin with the number of times Andre Fabre had trained the winner of the Prix de l'Arc de Triomphe up to and including Waldgeist in 2019

Multiply by the number of times Kauto Star won the King George VI Chase

Subtract the number of races in Altior's unbeaten run which began in October 2015

Divide by the number of winners ridden by Frankie Dettori at Ascot on 28 September 1996

What is the number you have arrived at?

Is it:

A. The number of times Pat Eddery rode the winner of the 2,000 Guineas?

B. The number of times Lester Piggott rode the winner of the 2,000 Guineas?

C. The number of times Willie Carson rode the winner of the 2,000 Guineas?

FILL IN THE BLANKS

Can you fill in the ten blanks below? Each blank may be one word, or the full name of a person, a horse or a race.

11.

The Irish Derby in _____ was won by the 4-11 favourite, _____. It was the second win in the race for his trainer, _____, and the first for his jockey, _____. The horse in third place, _____, had been runner-up to the winner in the Epsom Derby and had earlier won the _____ at Newmarket. In seventh place, at 66-1, was _____, who later that season had the first of four consecutive wins in the _____. What was to be the winner's final success came in his next race, the _____, which he won by two lengths from Fantastic Light. Subsequently, the winner became best known for his exceptional success as a _____.

12.

_____, ridden by Rachael Blackmore, won the _____ at the Cheltenham Festival in 2020. She had won all _____ of her previous starts. These included the Hatton's Grace Hurdle at _____ and the Irish Champion Hurdle at _____, both Grade Ones. The Cheltenham race was the first time since her racecourse debut when she did not start _____. The winner in 2018, _____, ridden by _____, started odds-on favourite and finished second, half a length behind the winner; in 2019 she fell at the last with the race at her mercy, leaving _____, who was _____ in 2020, to win.

GET IT IN ONE? OR TWO, OR THREE, OR FOUR

How few clues do you need to identify each of these famous jockeys?

11.

He was born in June 1985 and grew up in County Armagh.

He began his career as an apprentice with Curragh trainer Kevin Prendergast but his weight ruled out continuing as a flat jockey.

His first Grade One win was in the Ascot Chase on Waiting Patiently in 2018.

He became the first champion jump jockey based in the north of England since Jonjo O'Neill in 1980.

12.

He rode his first winner under National Hunt Rules, Rolyat, trained by Toby Balding, in an amateur riders' handicap hurdle at Exeter in August 1978.

He won the Champion Hurdle and the Queen Mother Champion Chase but not the Cheltenham Gold Cup.

He was son of and father of a jockey.

His last ride, on Sweet Duke at Ascot in April 1993, was a winner and set a record for career wins of 1,678.

WHERE'S THE LOGIC?

11.

Schubert finished runner-up to Chopin in the feature race. Monteverdi finished in between the mounts of Wilson and Owen, whilst Wagner finished in between Schubert and the mount of Stott. Morgan rode the horse that finished last of six and Rees rode the winner. Cullinan's ride made the early running and Ravel started favourite. Only one jockey rode a horse who shared the same first letter in their name.
Who rode Offenbach?

12.

The race for two-year-olds had just four runners – Jupiter, Mars, Neptune and Venus. They each had different colours – one was predominantly red, another yellow, one green and one blue. Each had a different trainer; Nolan trained the favourite.
Neptune trained by Price finished in front of the horse in yellow colours. Jupiter was not trained by Matthews. Matthews's horse finished in front of Mars, who was in red. Osborne's horse, in blue, came third.
Where did Venus finish?

TIME FOR A RHYME

Can you complete the missing rhymes in the poems
below and identify the jockey that the poem is about?

9.

Both Gosden and Godolphin recognised his spark

His father was a leading jockey in _____

He won the Derby in the silks of royal blue

Of 2020 jockeys he was number _____

10.

On the flat and over jumps, winners aplenty

Entered the 2,000 club in _____

On the flying Battaash he wins top sprints with ease

Had an Eclipse win and Arc third on _____

11.

2,000 and 1,000 Guineas, he's won both

His first Derby win was in 99 on _____

Two Arcs on Dylan Thomas and Hurricane Run

Now hopes his successes will be matched by his _____

12.

His dad for Swindon Town was a football player

He captured the Gold Cup on a famous _____

In the Guineas he beat Frankie by a short head

Now he has swapped the saddle for TV _____

SIMPLE SUMS

13.

Begin with the number of furlongs in the Cambridgeshire Handicap

Multiply by the number of letters in the name of the 2018 winner of the Epsom Derby

Subtract the number of fences jumped in the Ryanair Chase

Divide by the number of consecutive years that Paul Nicholls was champion jump trainer starting in the 2005-06 season

What is the number you have arrived at?

Is it:

A. The number of English Classic winners trained by Aidan O'Brien in 2016?

B. The number of English Classic winners trained by Aidan O'Brien in 2017?

C. The number of English Classic winners trained by Aidan O'Brien in 2018?

14.

Begin with the age that Neptune Collonges was when he won the Grand National

Add the number of furlongs run in the Goodwood Cup

Divide by the number of times Pat Eddery rode the winner of the Epsom Derby

Subtract the number of times Hurricane Fly won the Champion Hurdle

What is the number you have arrived at?

Is it:

A. The number of consecutive Group Ones won by Frankel?

B. The number of consecutive Group Ones won by Rock of Gibraltar?

C. The number of consecutive Group Ones won by Black Caviar?

FILL IN THE BLANKS

Can you fill in the ten blanks below? Each blank may be one word, or the full name of a person, a horse or a race.

13.

_____ was the winner of the Cheltenham Gold Cup in _____, in the first of what were to be _____ appearances in the race. For the winner's trainer, _____, it was a third win in the race. The second horse, _____, who started odds-on favourite, was having his second of what were to be _____ runs in the race. Between them, they won the race _____ times. The horse in third, _____, was having the second of four tilts at the race; he was never closer than _____ but the last race of his career was to be his greatest success, when he won the 2012 _____ by a nose.

14.

None of the first three in the betting for the Champion Hurdle in _____ finished in the first three. The favourite, _____, gave a below-par performance to finish sixth. The second favourite at 5-2, _____, came fourth. The third favourite, _____ at 11-4, fell at the _____ hurdle. The race was won by _____, with Mark Walsh riding in the familiar emerald green with yellow hoops of _____. His winning margin of _____ lengths was a record for the race. For the second horse, _____, it was the _____ consecutive year of finishing second at the Cheltenham Festival. It was the winner's last race as he had to be put down following a freak accident in the following August.

GET IT IN ONE? OR TWO, OR THREE, OR FOUR?

How few clues do you need to identify each of these famous racehorses?

13.

He won his only race at two and his only race at three.

His first run as a four-year-old was a win in the Thirsk Hunt Cup Handicap.

One of his offspring was second in the Derby, Ascot Gold Cup, Goodwood Cup and Lonsdale Cup.

He was twice second in Group Ones to Frankel.

14.

His dam was Offshore Boom.

One of his most successful offspring was Society Rock.

He twice had stablemate Hawk Wing in second place.

He won seven consecutive Group Ones.

WHERE'S THE LOGIC?

13.

What Larks was having a frustrating season, finishing second in each of her five starts. She always found a different horse to beat her, whichever of the five courses she was running at. She was even odds-on when running at Easthill.

The horses that beat What Larks, in alphabetical order, are Aero Blue, Antique White, Honeydew, Pink Flamingo and Shocking Pink. The distances she was beaten were a head, a neck, two, three and five lengths.

At Denley, when she was beaten by Shocking Pink, it was not by a head. She was beaten a neck at Bowminster, but not by Aero Blue. She was beaten five lengths by Honeydew, but not at Armfield. When she was second to Pink Flamingo at Cornham it was not by a head or by three lengths.

Which horse did What Larks come closest to beating?

14.

A jockey had a ride in each of the first four races. Each horse started at a different price but only one was favourite, at 6-4. The ride of hers that she fancied most was Coral. Each finished in the first three, except for one who was last.

In the second race, she finished third. She rode the 9-4 chance in the third race; that wasn't Aspect, who won his race. The 11-4 shot was not her ride in the first. Divine started at 7-4. Her ride in the fourth was Bauble, who did not finish second.

What was the price of the horse who finished last?

TELL ME THE ANSWER AND I'LL TELL YOU THE QUESTION

In each set of two questions and two answers below, only one of the answers is correct for only one of the questions. Can you find the matching pair?

13.

Questions

Which race named after a monarch was first run under that name in 1921?

Which race named after a monarch was first run under that name in 1926?

Answers

King George Stakes

Queen Mary Stakes

14.

Questions

Since 1970, which champion flat jockey had six years between his first and last championship?

Since 1970, which champion flat jockey had 11 years between his first and last championship?

Answers

Willie Carson

Pat Eddery

15.

Questions

Which race at Kempton, named after a winner of the King George VI Chase, is run over a distance of two miles four and a half furlongs? Which race at Kempton, named after a winner of the King George VI Chase, is run over a distance of three miles?

Answers

Silviniaco Conti Chase

Desert Orchid Chase

16.

Questions

Which Grand National winner of the 1990s was ridden by Tony Dobbin?

Which Grand National winner of the 1990s was ridden by Nigel Hawke?

Answers

Seagram

Royal Athlete

SIMPLE SUMS

15.

Begin with the number of races in Stradivarius's unbeaten run which began in May 2018

Multiply by the number of times that Frankie Dettori was champion flat jockey in the 1990s

Subtract the number of times Master Minded won the Queen Mother Champion Chase

Divide by the number of fillies who won the St Leger between 1945 and 2000

What is the number you have arrived at?

Is it:

A.   The number of times Badsworth Boy won the Queen Mother Champion Chase?

B.   The number of times Moscow Flyer won the Queen Mother Champion Chase?

C.   The number of times Sire de Grugy won the Queen Mother Champion Chase?

16.

Begin with the number of times that Yeats won the Goodwood Cup

Multiply by the number of complete furlongs in the Lonsdale Cup at York

Divide by the number of Epsom Derby winners sired by Montjeu

Subtract the number of racecourses in Nottinghamshire

What is the number you have arrived at?

Is it:

A.   The age at which Kauto Star won his first Ascot Chase?

B.   The age at which Kauto Star won his first King George VI Chase?

C.   The age at which Kauto Star won his first Cheltenham Gold Cup?

FILL IN THE BLANKS

Can you fill in the ten blanks below? Each blank may be one word or the full name of a person, a horse or a race.

15.

_____ won the _____ in 2020. The race was the first Group One race at the _____ meeting. He won by a head from the _____-trained Terebellum. Further back in the field were the 2018 winner of the race, _____, and the winner of the 2018 1,000 Guineas, _____. It was the winner's third Group One success, following the _____ at the same meeting the year before and the Prix du Moulin de Longchamp. The winner's _____ racecourse appearance, later that year, was when he was a _____ second to stable companion Order of Australia in the _____.

16.

_____ won the Betfair Chase in _____. It was the first of his five attempts in the race, which resulted in three wins, one _____ and one _____. In third place was Silviniaco Conti, who also ran five times in the race, resulting in two wins, in _____ and _____. Two Cheltenham Gold Cup winners were out of the first three: _____, winner in 2011, and _____, who started favourite for this, his first race since winning the Gold Cup earlier in the year. Another top-class chaser out of the frame was Silviniaco Conti's stablemate _____, who had his Cheltenham Festival win five years earlier in the _____.

GET IT IN ONE? OR TWO, OR THREE, OR FOUR?

How few clues do you need to identify each of these famous racehorses?

15.

He started at 200-1 in the 2010 Neptune Baring Bingham at the Cheltenham Festival and finished sixth of 17.

He appeared at the next six Cheltenham Festivals, always in chases.

His highest grade win was in Grade Two Argento Chase (Registered as the Cotswold Steeple Chase) in 2014.

He was second, fourth and third in three consecutive Cheltenham Gold Cups.

16.

This horse, who enjoyed great success under both rules, was sired by a winner of the Breeders' Cup Mile.

His wins included the Scottish Champion Hurdle and three novice chases.

He was second to his stable companion in the Chester Cup, second in the Champion Hurdle and second to Special Tiara in the Maghull Novices chase at Aintree.

He won the Northumberland Plate and the Fighting Fifth Hurdle.

WHERE'S THE LOGIC?

15.

The five runners in the sprint handicap were each of a different age – four, five, six, seven and eight. Each had fared differently last time out – one won, one was second, one was third, one fourth and the other unplaced. And each wore different headgear – blinkers, hood, cheekpieces, noseband and visor. Lancelot was favourite.

The horse a year younger than Merlin wore a visor and was unplaced last time out. The horse a year older than Merlin was third last time out. Either Merlin or Gawain was wearing blinkers and neither of them won last time out. The seven-year-old Bedivere was not wearing cheekpieces. The eight-year-old wearing a hood was not Tristan who was fourth last time out.

Who wore cheekpieces?

16.

Four horses, each with different sires, are in a row of stables, numbered one, two, three and four. The horses' names are Avatar, Fake News, Influencer and Cancel Culture, but they are not necessarily stabled in this order. Each is of a different colour.

Cancel Culture is sired by Bucephalus and is not the black horse in stable one. Pegasus is the sire of the horse in stable four. Influencer is in stable two and is not brown. Fake News is grey. Marengo is not the sire of the bay.

Which stable houses the progeny of Copenhagen?

TIME FOR A RHYME

Can you complete the missing rhymes in the poems below and identify the horse that the poem is about?

13.

The Dubai World Cup saw him achieve great glory

His jockey in nine out of ten was _____

In nine races, no doubt about the outcome

He lost only once, in the Derby at _____

14.

At Newmarket in May she had a sparkling win

First 1,000 for the colours of _____

As Epsom favourite she was nowhere to be seen

Eventually finishing nine of _____

15.

Described by the monarch as one of her best stars

It was appropriate that she won the _____

Then led one out and under strong pressure stayed on

To win the Gold Cup by a neck from _____

16.

Unplaced in the Guineas at 100-1

Later in 05 he was clearly _____

Won first outing next year in Dubai Duty Free

Eclipse after that was Group One win number _____

SIMPLE SUMS

17.

Begin with the number of letters in the name of the Aidan O' Brien-trained 2002 Epsom Derby winner

Multiply by the number of times Enable won the Yorkshire Oaks

Add the number of times Hardy Eustace won the Champion Hurdle

Divide by the number of races won by Frankel

What is the number you have arrived at?

Is it:

A. The number of racecourses in Warwickshire?

B. The number of racecourses in Berkshire?

C. The number of racecourses in Shropshire?

18.

Begin with the age that Best Mate was when he won his first Cheltenham Gold Cup

Multiply by the number of times Stradivarius had won the Ascot Gold Cup up to and including his 2020 victory

Divide by the number of times Willie Carson rode the winner of the St Leger

Add the number of letters in the name of the 2020 British Champions Long Distance Cup winner

What is the number you have arrived at?

Is it:

A. The number of Group One races won by Black Caviar?

B. The number of Group One races won by Frankel?

C. The number of Group One races won by Goldikova?

FILL IN THE BLANKS

Can you fill in the ten blanks below? Each blank may be one word or the full name of a person, a horse or a race.

17.

The _____ Stakes in 2015, run over _____ and a half furlongs at _____, was won by _____ at 50-1, by a neck from the 4-9 favourite, _____, ridden by _____. The Grey Gatsby was third. The winner was ridden by _____, for whom it was a first win in the race. For the winning trainer, _____, it was a second win, having won it previously in 1990 with _____. It was the first of two defeats that season for the beaten favourite; he was later second to _____ in the Breeders' Cup Turf.

18.

The _____ at Wetherby in 2016 was won by _____, ridden by Jonathan Moore and trained by _____. It was the highest grade race that the horse won. The previous year's winner, _____, was third. In second place was the winner from two years before, _____, who was notable for being a four times winner (2014-17) of the _____ at Sandown. He had also won the _____ at the Cheltenham Festival in 2010. Back in fourth was _____, the winner earlier in the year of the _____ at the Cheltenham Festival, who six months later would finish fourth in the Grand National to _____.

GET IT IN ONE? OR TWO, OR THREE, OR FOUR?

How few clues do you need to identify these famous trainers?

17.

She was Horserace Writers' and Photographers' National Hunt Trainer of the Year in 2002.

She trained the winner of the Peterborough Chase at Huntingdon for five consecutive years.

Her books include *Starting From Scratch: Inspired to be a Jump Jockey*.

Her best-known horse won six Grade Ones.

18.

Born in Gisburn, Yorkshire, 3 February 1950, his father and grandfather before him, and his mother after, were trainers.

He began training in 1980, taking over the licence at Poplar House in Harewood, West Yorkshire, and housing a maximum of 55 horses.

He was Champion Jumps Trainer three times.

He trained Ashley House who finished fifth in 1983 Cheltenham Gold Cup.

WHERE'S THE LOGIC?

17.

Callaghan started favourite of the four runners for the novice chase. They made for an unpromising field, as each had failed to complete in their last race, having either fallen, been pulled up, unseated their rider or refused. However, on this occasion, they all had a clear round! Baldwin was trained by North. The one trained by Moran unseated their rider last time out. The one who fell last time out this time finished fourth.

Asquith, who didn't win, refused last time out. Disraeli was second – he was not the one who pulled up last time; the one who did pull up was not trained by Parkes. Quinn trained the third.

Who trained the winner?

18.

The last race on the card was over a mile and had ten runners. Remarkably, the first five horses in the betting were the last five horses home. The sixth was two lengths in front of the seventh, who was one length ahead of the eighth, who was two lengths ahead of the ninth with one length back to the tenth and last!

The favourite didn't finish ninth. Oscar didn't finish sixth. Golf was two lengths behind the second favourite but finished in front of Lima. A horse that was next to Alfa in the betting was a length behind Alfa in the race.

In the betting Sierra was fourth and behind Golf.

Where was Lima in the betting?

TELL ME THE ANSWER AND I'LL TELL YOU THE QUESTION

In each set of two questions and two answers below, only one of the answers is correct for only one of the questions. Can you find the matching pair?

17.

Questions

Which dual winner of the Chester Cup had their first win in 1995?

Which dual winner of the Chester Cup had their first win in 1999?

Answers

Rainbow High

Anak Pekan

18.

Questions

Which grey won the Ascot Chase in 1998?

Which grey won the Ascot Chase in 1999?

Answers

Teeton Mill

Monet's Garden

19.

Questions

Which Oaks winner ridden by Ryan Moore won the Pretty Polly Stakes on her next outing?

Which Oaks winner ridden by Ryan Moore won the Yorkshire Oaks on her next outing?

Answers

Minding

Snow Fairy

20.

Questions

Which horse beat Commanche Court into second place to win the Cheltenham Gold Cup?

Which horse beat Take the Stand into second place to win the Cheltenham Gold Cup?

Answers

War of Attrition

Kicking King

SIMPLE SUMS

19.

Begin with the number of times Martin Pipe was champion jump trainer

Multiply by the number of times Best Mate won the King George VI Chase

Add the number of Group Ones normally run in a season at Sandown Park

Divide by the number of times that Dahlia won the King George VI and Queen Elizabeth Stakes

What is the number you have arrived at?

Is it:

A. The number of letters in the name of the 2018 winner of the Epsom Oaks?

B. The number of letters in the name of the 2019 winner of the Epsom Oaks?

C. The number of letters in the name of the 2020 winner of the Epsom Oaks?

20.

Begin with the number of times Brigadier Gerard won the Champion Stakes

Multiply by the number of stones Hoof It carried to victory in the 2011 Stewards' Cup

Add the number of furlongs in the Victoria Cup

Divide by the number of times Steve Cauthen was champion flat jockey

What is the number you have arrived at?

Is it:

A. The age of Kicking King when he won the Cheltenham Gold Cup?

B. The age of Looks Like Trouble when he won the Cheltenham Gold Cup?

C. The age of Synchronised when he won the Cheltenham Gold Cup?

FILL IN THE BLANKS

Can you fill in the ten blanks below? Each blank may be one word or the full name of a person, a horse or a race.

19.

The Epsom Derby in _____ was won by _____ who was ridden by _____ and started at 40-1. In second place was the winner's stablemate, Cliffs of Moher. In third was _____, who went on to win the Champion Stakes that season and again the following season. Another stable companion was _____, in sixth, who went on to Group One wins in that season's _____ and _____. The high quality of the field was also in evidence in Benbatl, who finished fifth, and Best Solution, who finished eighth, as both went on to win Group Ones. _____, who beat only _____ horses home, won the _____ at Flemington later that year.

20.

The World Hurdle at the Cheltenham Festival in _____ was unusual because of the presence amongst the riders of a top-class jockey from the flat – _____. He rode _____, who was beaten a head into second place by _____. The winner returned to the Festival the following year to take the _____. On his eventual return to hurdling, he contested the World Hurdle again in 2008 but could finish only fifth behind _____ who was winning it for the _____ time. Fifth in 2006 was _____, who was having his fifth and final run in the race, following two seconds and two wins in _____ and _____, when the race was known as the Stayers' Hurdle.

GET IT IN ONE? OR TWO, OR THREE, OR FOUR?

How few clues do you need to identify these famous trainers?

19.

He was born into a farming family in Lanarkshire in December 1966 and competed on the show jumping circuit before joining David Nicholson as an amateur jockey in 1985.

He moved in June 2000 to the Barbury Castle estate near Marlborough, Wiltshire.

His first Cheltenham Festival win was the William Hill Trophy Handicap Chase in 2004 with Fork Lightning ridden by Robert Thornton.

He had three winners at Royal Ascot 2020 with Coeur De Lion, Scarlet Dragon and Who Dares Wins successful.

20.

As a youth he was regularly found at his local racecourse, Garrison Savannah.

His first win as a trainer came when Sandal, a horse owned by his father, won at Newmarket.

He trained Kribensis to win the Champion Hurdle in 1990.

In 2013 he trained the Queen's Ascot Gold Cup winner Estimate.

WHERE'S THE LOGIC?

19.

The trainer Price had four of the ten runners in the six-furlong sprint. Each wore a different type of headgear. One of them started favourite, ridden by Driver.

Of these four runners, Boyne rode the horse with the hood; Allen rode Morgana, who was not the trainer's horse drawn eight; Cook's mount was drawn one – he was not on Nantucket who wore cheekpieces; the horse with a noseband was drawn four; Penelope was drawn ten. What headgear was worn by Opal?

20.

Each of the horses in the row of stables numbered one, two, three and four is of a different age.

In stable two is either the six-year-old or the eight-year-old. Porthos is not the seven or eight-year-old. Aramis is next to D'Artagnan, whilst Athos or Porthos is in stable four. The seven-year-old is next to the nine-year-old.

There is a horse in between Aramis and Athos. The number of Athos's stable is one higher than the number of the eight-year-old's stable. What is the name of the six-year-old?

TIME FOR A RHYME

Can you complete the missing rhymes in the poems below and identify the trainer that the poem is about?

17.

The first winner he trained was the last that he rode

Since then, from Beechdown stables his winners have _____

Speedy sprinters are still his speciality

But second Middle Park came with _____

18.

With Henbit, Nashwan, Troy, three Derbys did he win

Six Legers too, one for the Queen with _____

His third St Leger win was with bold Bustino

The best he trained was beaten once, by _____

19.

Thomas, Walsh, Fitzgerald rode his Gold Cup first three

An eighth King George came with _____

His 12th King George win was in 20 with Frodon

He enjoys a win at local course _____

20.

From a quiet start as a trainer, he went far

And produced a National winner for _____

He broke all the training records over the sticks

And even at Royal Ascot his wins numbered _____

SIMPLE SUMS

21.

Begin with the number of times Persian War won the Champion Hurdle

Multiply by the number of winners ridden by Holly Doyle at Windsor on 29 August 2020

Add the number of fences jumped before the Foinavon in the Grand National

Subtract the number of complete furlongs run in the Cesarewitch Handicap.

What is the number you have arrived at?

Is it:

A. The number of times Master Minded won the Clarence House Chase?

B. The number of times Sire De Grugy won the Clarence House Chase?

C. The number of times Un De Sceaux won the Clarence House Chase?

22.

Begin with the number of letters in the name of the winner of the 2018 King George VI Chase

Multiply by the number of racecourses in Merseyside

Subtract the age that Notnowcato was when he won the Eclipse Stakes

Divide by the number of times that See You Then won the Champion Hurdle

What is the number you have arrived at?

Is it:

A. The number of letters in the name of the winner of the Irish Derby in 2017?

B. The number of letters in the name of the winner of the Irish Derby in 2018?

C. The number of letters in the name of the winner of the Irish Derby in 2019?

FILL IN THE BLANKS

Can you fill in the ten blanks below? Each blank may be one word or the full name of a person, a horse or a race.

21.

_____, the winner of the St Leger in _____, subsequently won only one more race, a Group Three. However, the next four horses home all went on to great success. The second, _____, won the Prince of Wales's Stakes as a five-year-old and was twice beaten by a neck in the _____. _____ trained both the third, _____, who was unbeaten in the following season and became the leading stayer in Britain, and the fifth, _____, who won two Group Ones in_____ as a five-year-old. Fourth was _____, trained by _____, who on his next run won the Melbourne Cup.

22.

The _____ in 2015 was won by Identity Thief, trained by _____. Later in the season he was sixth in the Champion Hurdle behind _____, while his only other Grade One success was to come in the Ryanair Stayers' Hurdle at _____ in 2018. He beat Top Notch by a neck at Newcastle and ten lengths away in third was _____, a talented performer under both rules who, in the following year, won the _____ from the 1-7 favourite Order of St George and seven months later the _____ from My Tent Or Yours. Sixth at Newcastle was _____, who had won the race in _____ and was to take it again in _____.

GET IT IN ONE? OR TWO, OR THREE, OR FOUR?

How few clues do you need to identify these famous jockeys?

21.

He was Champion Conditional jockey for the 2008-09 season.

He became one of the youngest jockeys to ride in the Grand National when in 2008, as a 19-year-old, he rode Mon Mome.

His first Cheltenham Festival winner was in 2009 aboard Venetia Williams's Kayf Aramis.

His first Grade One win was in the Long Walk Hurdle in 2018, when he rode Paisley Park to victory for Emma Lavelle.

22.

Born in Donegal in 1983, he served an apprenticeship with Dessie Hughes

His first Cheltenham Festival win was on Zarkander in the 2011 Triumph Hurdle.

He rode the winner of the Scilly Isles Novices' Chase for four years in a row, starting in 2015.

His biggest win came in the 2012 Grand National.

WHERE'S THE LOGIC?

21.

The first four home in the last race each had a different trainer – Matthews, Nolan, Osborne and Price – and each had a different sire. The runner trained by Matthews finished fourth – this was not the filly sired by Abacus. Nolan trained the gelding and Osborne trained the runner sired by Divide. The colt won. The runner sired by Calculus is not the mare and was not second.

Where did the gelding finish? Who trained the offspring of Biometric?

22.

Conqueror was a horse living up to his name. He had won his first four races of the season. His first win was in a tight finish with Rivalry and the subsequent three were tight finishes too. For each win he had a different jockey and a different SP: 2-1, 3-1, 4-1 and 5-1

When he was 2-1, he won by a short head; when he was 3-1, he beat Steerforth into second. When he beat Triangulate it was by a nose; this was not when he was ridden by Boyne starting at 5-1. Unicorn was not the one beaten a head by Conqueror and not the one in second when Conqueror was ridden by Allen. When Driver was the jockey, Conqueror won by a neck.

What distance did Conqueror win by when Cook rode him?

TELL ME THE ANSWER AND I'LL TELL YOU THE QUESTION

In each set of two questions and two answers below, only one of the answers is correct for only one of the questions. Can you find the matching pair?

21.

Questions

Which of the five racecourses in North Yorkshire is the northernmost?

Which of the five racecourses in North Yorkshire is the southernmost?

Answers

Catterick

York

22.

Questions

US Army Ranger started favourite for the Epsom Derby and finished second to which horse?

Fame and Glory started favourite for the Epsom Derby and finished second to which horse?

Answers

Sea the Stars

High Chaparral

23.

Questions

Which jockey rode his first 2,000 Guineas winner on a horse trained by Michael Stoute?

Which jockey rode his first 2,000 Guineas winner on a horse trained by Richard Hannon Snr?

Answers

Johnny Murtagh

Michael Kinane

24.

Questions

Which horse was the first five-year-old to win the Coronation Cup after 2000?

Which horse was the first six-year-old to win the Coronation Cup after 2000?

Answers

Boreal

Warsaan

SIMPLE SUMS

23.

Begin with the number of hurdles jumped in the Ballymore Novices' Hurdle

Add the number of furlongs run in the July Cup

Divide by the number of times Bronze Angel won the Cambridgeshire Handicap

Subtract the number of times Frankie Dettori rode the winner of the Oaks, up to and including 2020

What is the number you have arrived at?

Is it:

A.   The number of times Oscar Whisky won the Aintree Hurdle?

B.   The number of times Al Eile won the Aintree Hurdle?

C.   The number of times The New One won the Aintree Hurdle?

24.

Begin with the number of stones carried to victory by Burrough Hill Lad in the 1984 Hennessy Cognac Gold Cup

Add the number of times Kieren Fallon rode the winner of the Epsom Derby

Multiply by the number of times See More Business won the King George VI Chase

Divide by the number of stones carried to victory by Cloth Cap in the 2020 Ladbrokes Trophy

What is the number you have arrived at?

Is it:

A.   The number of times Reve De Sivola won the Long Walk Hurdle up to and including 2020?

B.   The number of times Thistlecrack won the Long Walk Hurdle up to and including 2020?

C.   The number of times Paisley Park won the Long Walk Hurdle up to and including 2020?

FILL IN THE BLANKS

Can you fill in the ten blanks below? Each blank may be one word or the full name of a person, a horse or a race.

23.

The Nunthorpe Stakes at York in _____ was won by Mecca's Angel, ridden by _____, who would ride her on her second victory in the race in _____. In second place was the 13-8 favourite, _____, trained in the USA by _____. Out of the placings were no less than three past and future winners of the King's Stand Stakes at Royal Ascot. In fourth place was _____, winner of the King's Stand Stakes in 2013 and 2014, as well as the Nunthorpe Stakes in _____ and 2014. In fifth was _____, who won the King's Stand Stakes in his race before the Nunthorpe and won the _____ on his next appearance. In tenth place, at 20-1, was _____, who went on to victory in the Royal Ascot sprint the following year.

24.

The _____ at Ascot in 2020 was won by _____, ridden by _____, by a _____ from Thyme Hill. In doing so, he reversed the placings from when the pair previously met in the Long Distance Hurdle at _____ just 22 days earlier where he finished second, beaten one and a half lengths. For the winner, it was a _____ Grade One success, the first having been in this race _____ years previously. Third was _____, who had won the David Nicholson Mares' Hurdle at the Cheltenham Festival in 2019. In sixth place was the 2019 winner of the race, _____, while last of the seven finishers was _____, who had won his previous nine races, all in handicap company.

GET IT IN ONE? OR TWO, OR THREE, OR FOUR?

How few clues do you need to identify these famous jockeys?

23.

He was born in Brighton in 1985 with a father who was a jockey and a grandfather who was a trainer.

He was Champion Conditional Jockey in 2004.

He won Scottish Grand National 40-1 in 2014.

He won five Grade One chases on Sire de Grugy.

24.

His grandfather was a former Lord Mayor of London.

The charities he supports includes the running of Tom's Ward, a children's unit at Oxford's John Radcliffe Hospital named after his younger brother, Thomas, who died from cancer in 2004, aged 20.

The first of his several wins over the Grand National fences was in the 2005 Foxhunters' on Katarino.

He rode the winner of the Cheltenham Gold Cup in the same year as riding the second in the Grand National.

WHERE'S THE LOGIC?

23.

The Flat Jockey Championship had seen the same four jockeys – Allen, Boyne, Cook and Driver – fill the first four places for the last five years, but never in the same order.

Allen was the only one not to win yet; he had always finished second. Driver had won just once, when Cook had been fourth. This year it was the same first four and Allen was second again! However, they still finished in an order in which they had not finished in the previous five years.

Can you work out the placings?

24.

The horse named Goodtogo had gained a reputation for being best when fresh. He had won on his first race of the season for each of the last four seasons. These wins had been at four different courses, Armfield, Bowminster, Cornham and Denley, and on four different types of going, firm, good, good to soft and soft. Furthermore, on each of these occasions he had been in a different place in the first four in the betting.

His fourth winning debut had been at Armfield. In his first winning seasonal debut the going was firm; this was not when he started as third favourite at Cornham. His opening success in the third season was not the one at Denley on good going. He started favourite when his debut was on soft. In the second of these wins, he did not start second favourite.

Where did he win when he was second favourite?

TIME FOR A RHYME

Can you complete the missing rhymes in the poems below and identify the jockey that the poem is about?

21.

With Botti and Varian his talent he's honed

Winning Ascot's King George and QE on _____

Having arrived in England when just 17

He had won two St Legers by _____

22.

Top rider for Hannons senior and junior

Won on seven out of eight one day at _____

Champion Hurdler Monksfield was ridden by dad

He won the Irish version riding _____

23.

Won the Betfair by 11 on Agrapart

First in the Ultima on _____

Into the record books when riding Tea for Two

In July 2020 time to say, _____

24.

A first Grade One in the 2015 Challow

Another in the Clarence House aboard _____

Has ridden for Pauling, Bailey and Henderson

In the 16 National, beaten by only _____

SIMPLE SUMS

25.

Begin with the age that Cirrus des Aigles was when he won the Champion Stakes

Multiply by the number of times Denman finished second in the Cheltenham Gold Cup

Add the number of letters in the name of the winner of the 2020 Charlie Hall Chase

Divide by the number of times Lester Piggott rode the winner of the Ascot Gold Cup

What is the number you have arrived at?

Is it:

A. The number of Epsom Derby winners trained by John Oxx?

B. The number of Epsom Derby winners trained by Dick Hern?

C. The number of Epsom Derby winners trained by Henry Cecil?

26.

Begin with the number of letters in the name of the 2015 2,000 Guineas winner

Multiply by the number of times Double Trigger won the Doncaster Cup

Divide by the number of times Frankie Dettori had won the Prix de l'Arc de Triomphe up to and including Enable's second win

Subtract the number of racecourses in Devon

What is the number you have arrived at?

Is it:

A. The number of English Classics won by Nijinsky?

B. The number of English Classics won by Sea the Stars?

C. The number of English Classics won by Galileo?

FILL IN THE BLANKS

Can you fill in the ten blanks below? Each blank may be one word or the full name of a person, a horse or a race.

25.

The winner of the _____ in 2010 was _____. Trained by _____ and ridden by Olivier Peslier, he won by 11 lengths and in a course record time. In second place was Cape Blanco who on his previous outing had won the _____ and on his next outing won the _____. In third place was _____, who had finished second in each of the last three runnings of the _____. The winner's stable companion, _____, started odds-on favourite but could only finish _____. The race was to be the winner's last. Just _____ weeks after his victory he suffered a fractured leg on the gallops and was retired.

26.

The _____ Eclipse Stakes was won by _____. The winning jockey, _____, made a daring manoeuvre by taking the winner alone up the stands' side of the course and he rode another _____ winners on the card. He won by a length and a half from Authorized, ridden by _____, who on his previous outing had won the _____ by _____ lengths. In third place was _____, who had won the previous season's 2,000 Guineas. The second had his revenge on the winner later in the season when he won the _____ at York, with the Eclipse winner in _____ place.

GET IT IN ONE? OR TWO, OR THREE, OR FOUR?

How few clues do you need to identify these famous jockeys?

25.

In his racecourse debut he won a maiden at Nottingham in July 2010 by nine lengths.

In his second Group One win as a two-year-old he won by nine lengths.

In a total of five Group One wins all but one were over six furlongs.

He gave Hayley Turner her first Group One winner in the July Cup.

26.

He was beaten only once (by a head) in eight races.

He won the Irish Derby by nine lengths.

One of his offspring was second in three consecutive Prix de l'Arc de Triomphes.

He was the first horse to win the Epsom Derby, Irish Derby Stakes and Prix de l'Arc de Triomphe in the same year.

WHERE'S THE LOGIC?

25.

Moran the trainer had high hopes for her runners in the first four races. She had one in each of the races and none of them had won last time out; they had been either second, third, fourth or unplaced. Unfortunately, on this occasion, none of them even finished! One fell, one pulled up, one unseated his rider and one was unlucky enough to be carried out!

The one who was second last time out ran in the race following the one where the trainer's horse was pulled up. The one who was carried out was in the race after the horse who was fourth last time out. The one who fell was in the first three last time out. The one who was unplaced last time out did not run in the second or third race. The horse who was unplaced last time out ran immediately before the one who was fourth last time out.

In which race did the trainer's horse unseat his rider?

26.

There were five runners in the feature race of the day. The winner was not drawn one and was least fancied of the five runners in the betting. The second in the betting was drawn four. Number three on the racecard was drawn five. The horse who finished fourth was drawn two. Number five on the racecard was not third. Number two on the racecard, who was not third in the betting, finished second. The one who was third in the betting finished in front of number one on the racecard. Number four on the racecard, who was also fourth in the market, finished in front of the horse drawn three.

What number on the racecard was the favourite and where did he finish?

TELL ME THE ANSWER AND I'LL TELL YOU THE QUESTION

In each set of two questions and two answers below, only one of the answers is correct for only one of the questions. Can you find the matching pair?

25.

Questions

Which race named after a royal residence was first run under that name in 1834?

Which race named after a royal residence was first run under that name in 1946?

Answers

The Sandringham Stakes

The Royal Lodge Stakes

26.

Questions

Which jockey rode the winner when Aidan O'Brien trained the first three in the Irish Derby in 2011?

Which jockey rode the winner when Aidan O'Brien trained the first three in the Irish Derby in 2019?

Answers

Colm O'Donoghue

Joseph O'Brien

27.

Questions

Which five-year-old won the Tingle Creek Chase in 2005?
Which five-year-old won the Tingle Creek Chase in 2007?

Answers

Kauto Star
Master Minded

28.

Questions

Which rider of back-to-back winners of the St Leger this century rode
the second of those winners for trainer Jeremy Noseda?
Which rider of back-to-back winners of the St Leger this century rode
the second of those winners for trainer John Gosden?

Answers

Andrea Atzeni
Frankie Dettori

SIMPLE SUMS

27.

Begin with the number of times that Lester Piggott rode the winner of the Epsom Derby

Multiply by the number of times that Swain won the King George VI and Queen Elizabeth Stakes

Subtract the number of times that Istabraq won the Champion Hurdle

Add the number of times that Peter Scudamore was champion jump jockey outright

What is the number you have arrived at?

Is it:

A.   The number of fences jumped in the King George VI Chase?

B.   The number of fences jumped in the Cheltenham Gold Cup?

C.   The number of fences jumped in the Betfair Chase?

28.

Begin with the age that Treve was when she won her second Prix de l'Arc de Triomphe

Multiply by the number of times that Sole Power won the King's Stand Stakes

Add the number of times Golden Miller won the Cheltenham Gold Cup

Subtract the number of hurdles jumped in the Stayers' Hurdle

What is the number you have arrived at?

Is it:

A.   The number of times that Peter Walwyn was champion flat trainer?

B.   The number of times that Dick Hern was champion flat trainer?

C.   The number of times that John Dunlop was champion flat trainer?

FILL IN THE BLANKS

Can you fill in the ten blanks below? Each blank may be one word or the full name of a person, a horse or a race.

27.

The _____ in 2015 was won by _____ from Shaneshill. The winning trainer, _____, was winning the race for the _____ consecutive year. For the winner, this was the third in a winning sequence of _____ since joining Willie Mullins (eight of which were Grade Ones), which came to an end in the Queen Mother Champion Chase _____ years later. For the third horse, _____, this was one of seven occasions when he was placed behind the winner. He came into his own, however, in 2017, when he won four Grade One chases – the _____, the _____, the _____ and the John Durkan Memorial Punchestown Chase.

28.

The _____-year-old _____ won the _____ at Newbury in _____. Ridden by _____, he won by three and a quarter lengths from Houblon Des Obeaux. Fourth was the winner of the Welsh Grand National in January 2013, _____. Favourite was the five-year-old _____ trained by Willie Mullins. He finished eighth and would go on to be second twice in the Cheltenham Gold Cup, first to _____ in 2015 and then to _____ in 2016. The winner went on to win the _____ later that season at 25-1 by one and three quarter lengths from Saint Are. He subsequently had a race at Aintree named after him.

GET IT IN ONE? OR TWO, OR THREE, OR FOUR?

How few clues do you need to identify these famous jockeys?

27.

He ran 40 times, winning five and coming second 15 times.

His first win was on his tenth outing in a maiden hurdle at Clonmel in February 2002.

In three consecutive races he was second in the Hennessy Cognac Gold Cup at Leopardstown then the Cheltenham Gold Cup and then the Grand National.

He gave Ruby Walsh his second Grand National winner.

28.

The sire of this National Hunt performer finished third in the Epsom Derby.

In his first chase at Cheltenham he won from future Grand National winner Don't Push It.

In his first three seasons under Rules, he won 13 out of 14, and in his last three, one out of ten.

He was three times second in the Cheltenham Gold Cup.

WHERE'S THE LOGIC?

27.

There was a feature race on each day of the three-day meeting at Denley. Each feature race was a different distance and had a different type of sponsor.

The bookmaker did not sponsor Friday's race. The finance company sponsored the sprint or the two-mile race. The sprint was on Friday or Saturday. Thursday's race sponsor was the brewery or the finance company. The bookmaker did not sponsor the sprint. Thursday's race was the mile or the sprint.

Who sponsored the mile race?

28.

Jamie backed one horse to win in each of five races on TV one afternoon. Only one of the selections won. The others were second, third, fourth and unplaced. The races were two handicaps, one over a mile and another over one mile and four furlongs; a race for two-year-olds; a race for three-year olds only; and a non-handicap over two miles.

Jamie's winner was not in the first race. Jamie's 3-1 runner was in the one-mile, four-furlongs handicap, the fifth race. In the one-mile handicap, Jamie's bet was third. The second race was the non-handicap for three-year-olds only.

The horse who was 6-4 came third; this was not in the first race but it was in an earlier race than the one where Jamie's choice came fourth. The unplaced horse was 5-4. The selection in the race for two-year-olds was 10-1. In the third race, Jamie's choice came second.

Where did Jamie's choice finish in the two-mile race? Where did the 8-1 bet finish?

TIME FOR A RHYME

Can you complete the missing rhymes in the poems below and identify the horse that the poem is about?

25.

He runs over five furlongs as quick as a flash
On three occasions he has won the _____
By the second win at Epsom, he was seven
He still won races at the age of _____

26.

Second in the 2,000 and just five years on
One better place by Footstepsinthesand, his _____
Five Group One wins in 12 weeks was a tour de force
And resulted in his nickname, _____

27.

Second in the Leger under Pat Eddery
She had produced a sixth Oaks win for _____
Her sire Diesis, her dam Princess of Man
Her 'Generous' owner – _____

28.

Twice a neck second in the King George and QE
His only Group One win came under _____
Six lengths second in the Champion to Cracksman
His last race at York was a second to _____

SIMPLE SUMS

29.

Begin with the number of letters in the name of the 2020 winner of the Arkle Challenge Trophy

Multiply by the number of times Silviniaco Conti won the Betfair Chase

Subtract the number of times Vinnie Roe won the Irish St Leger

Divide by the number of consecutive years that Aidan O' Brien was champion flat trainer, starting with the 2007 season

What is the number you have arrived at?

Is it:

A.   The age of Amberleigh House when he won the Grand National?

B.   The age of Red Marauder when he won the Grand National?

C.   The age of Don't Push It when he won the Grand National?

30.

Begin with the age that Faugheen was when he won the Champion Hurdle

Add the number of times that Sadler's Wells was champion sire in GB and Ireland

Multiply by the number of finishers in the 1928 Grand National

Divide by the number of times Quevega won the David Nicholson Mares' Hurdle

What is the number you have arrived at?

Is it:

A.   The age of Katchit when he won the Champion Hurdle?

B.   The age of Punjabi when he won the Champion Hurdle?

C.   The age of Hors La Loi III when he won the Champion Hurdle?

FILL IN THE BLANKS

Can you fill in the ten blanks below? Each blank may be one word, or the full name of a person, a horse or a race.

29.

The 2016 _____ was won by _____, ridden by _____. This was the first of his three appearances in the race. In 2017 he was beaten a short head by _____; in 2018, on his last racecourse appearance, he was _____ to Stradivarius. Later in 2016 he finished third in the Prix de l'Arc de Triomphe behind his stable companions _____ and _____. He returned in the following year to finish _____ behind _____. He also won the _____ in 2015 and 2017.

30.

_____ was an impressive winner of the _____ in 2018 at the Cheltenham Festival. Ridden by _____, he won by seven lengths from Monalee. The horse in third place later that year started 3-1 favourite and won the Welsh Grand National with the Cheltenham fourth, _____, back in sixth. This pair were to meet again in the 2019 _____ at Wetherby where it was _____'s turn to win, beating _____ by _____-and-three-quarter lengths. The runner at Cheltenham who had the greatest subsequent success was _____ who fell two out. He won his first _____ at the Festival the following year.

GET IT IN ONE? OR TWO, OR THREE, OR FOUR?

How few clues do you need to identify these famous trainers?

29.

His first winner as a trainer was La Dolce Vita at Thirsk, 18 April 1969.

He was born in Worcester in 1937, with the first names Barrington William.

He trained Steve Cauthen's first Classic winner.

His five children all went to work in racing.

30.

He moved into custom-built stables in 2013; they are named after the Goodwood race which gave him a first Group winner in 2006.

He was named International Trainer of the Year at the Horserace Writers' and Photographers' Association Derby Awards of 2012.

His first Royal Ascot winner came in 2018 in the Duke of Cambridge Stakes with Aljazzi.

Born in 1976, he is the son of a champion racehorse trainer in Italy.

WHERE'S THE LOGIC?

29.

In the last race on the card, Californium finished fifth, in front of Mercury who was last of the six runners. Strontium finished in between the horse trained by Moore and the horse trained by Murphy. Argon finished in between the horse trained by Coulthwaite and Californium.

The horse trained by Blackwell won and the one trained by Land was last.

Only one trainer and their horse had the same number of letters in their names. Anthony trained the favourite and Neon was the youngest horse in the field.

Who trained Silver?

30.

The horse Persistent was living up to his name this season. Fourth on his first outing, he was third next time, then second, and finally won on his fourth outing. The trainer put it down to experimenting with different headgear and he did try something different with each outing. On each of the four outings Persistent visited a different course and carried a different weight.

When he carried 8st 12lb he wore a hood; this was before his run at Bowminster. When he carried 8st 10lb he was not in blinkers. This was before he tried cheekpieces at Armfield. He carried 8st 9lb at Denley on his third outing and on his other run carried 8st 11lb.

On which outing did he wear a visor?

TELL ME THE ANSWER AND I'LL TELL YOU THE QUESTION

In each set of two questions and two answers below, only one of the answers is correct for only one of the questions. Can you find the matching pair?

29.

Questions

Which winner of the Gordon Stakes this century, who followed up with a win in the following season's King George VI and Queen Elizabeth Stakes, won the Breeders' Cup Turf in between?

Which winner of the Gordon Stakes this century, who followed up with a win in the following season's King George VI and Queen Elizabeth Stakes, won the Ormonde Stakes in between?

Answers

Highland Reel

Harbinger

30.

Questions

Which horse beat Kentucky Hyden into second place to win the Triumph Hurdle?

Which horse beat Top Notch into second place to win the Triumph Hurdle?

Answers

Our Conor

Tiger Roll

31.

Questions

Which novelist and former jockey wrote the novel *Taking the Fall*?
Which novelist and former jockey wrote the novel *False Start*?

Answers

Tony McCoy
Dick Francis

32.

Questions

Since 2001, which Grand National winner ran in the race the following year and finished third?
Since 2001, which Grand National winner ran in the race the following year and finished fourth?

Answers

Mon Mome
Monty's Pass

SIMPLE SUMS

31.

Begin with the age that Yeats was when he won his fourth Ascot Gold Cup

Multiply by the number of times Aaim To Prosper won the Cesarewitch Handicap.

Divide by the number of times Baracouda won the Long Walk Hurdle

Add the number of runners in the Epsom Derby won by Camelot

What is the number you have arrived at?

Is it:

A. The number of Grade One races won by Apple's Jade?

B. The number of Grade One races won by Kauto Star?

C. The number of Grade One races won by Moscow Flyer?

32.

Begin with the number of races won by the unbeaten Lammtarra

Add the number of times Willie Carson was champion flat jockey

Subtract the number of letters in the name of the winner of the 2020 Paddy Power Gold Cup

Add the number of Epsom Derby winners sired by Sadler's Wells

What is the number you have arrived at?

Is it:

A. The number of times Sprinter Sacre won the Tingle Creek Chase?

B. The number of times Kauto Star won the Tingle Creek Chase?

C. The number of times Flagship Uberalles won the Tingle Creek Chase?

FILL IN THE BLANKS

Can you fill in the ten blanks below? Each blank may be one word or the full name of a person, a horse or a race.

31.

The Irish St Leger in 2014 was won by the _____-year-old _____. It was the winner's second attempt in the race following a third place to _____ in 2012. Trained by _____ and ridden by _____, the winner won by six and a half lengths and a _____ from two previous Doncaster St Leger winners – _____, who had won the English Classic in the previous year, and _____, the winner in 2012. The winner's other big successes included the Group Two _____ in 2013 and the _____ in 2015.

32.

The seven-runner field for the 2016 Dewhurst Stakes included some horses who were to be top-class performers over the next three seasons. For the winner, _____, it was the second of _____ consecutive Group One wins – the next two were the 2017 _____ and the _____. The third, _____, went on to win the King's Stand Stakes at Royal Ascot in 2018 and both that race and the Diamond Jubilee Stakes at the 2019 Royal Ascot meeting. Also carrying the _____ colours, _____, in fourth, became the first horse to win two _____, in 2018 and 2019. Lancaster Bomber in second won the _____ in 2018, whilst Rivet Delight in fifth won the _____ on his next start.

GET IT IN ONE? OR TWO, OR THREE, OR FOUR?

How few clues do you need to identify these famous trainers?

31.

She was a top three-day event rider before taking out a training licence in 1987.

This trainer has sent out winners of the Champion Hurdle, Queen Mother Champion Chase and Cheltenham Gold Cup.

Group Ones won on the flat include the Cheveley Park Stakes and the Falmouth Stakes.

Her stables are in Moone, County Kildare.

32.

He achieved a BSc honours degree in Agriculture in 1975 at Reading University.

He had a successful career as a jockey riding 160 winners before turning his mind to training.

He began with a few horses down on the family farm at Sandhill in Somerset which were kept in a converted cowshed.

He trained Dream Alliance to win the 2009 Welsh Grand National and this was the inspiration for the 2020 film *Dream Horse*.

WHERE'S THE LOGIC?

31.

The last race on the card had five runners. The winner, who did not start at 3-1, was ridden by Bradshaw. The jockey on the 7-4 favourite was Carter. Quisling was second, but not ridden by Dunphy; Dunphy's ride finished in front of Titanium. Pandemonium was 16-1, while the horse who finished fourth was 5-1. Rousseau, who was ridden by Ashton, finished in front of the 5-2 shot. Sassafras was not third.

The other jockey was Earnshaw. Who did he ride and where did he finish?

32.

Alex backed five horses in ten doubles, ten trebles, five fourfolds and a fivefold accumulator. The horses were: Dutch Courage, French Exit, Roman Holiday, Spanish Armada and Swiss Roll. Their SPs were evens, 2-1, 4-1, 5-1 and 10-1. They all won! Each won by a different distance, the longest of which was five lengths.

Dutch Courage won at 2-1 and not by a length. The 4-1 won by half a length and it was not Swiss Roll. The 5-1 shot won by a nose; it was not Swiss Roll or Spanish Armada. French Exit won by a short head and was not evens.

Which horse was Alex's shortest price winner?

TIME FOR A RHYME

Can you complete the missing rhymes in the poems below and identify the trainer that the poem is about?

29.

He has runners on the flat and over the sticks

His magic gelding won the Chester Cup by _____

He's won at each course from Perth to Newton Abbot

Frankel's son supplied a first win at _____

30.

He is providing rides for his namesake and son

He achieved the ultimate double on _____

His horse won the Grand National for Tony McCoy

Two years later, was second with _____

31.

His first season as a trainer brought him much joy

Like a Cheltenham Festival win – _____

But in 2014 he had his greatest day

When he won the National with _____

32.

Son of a famous dad, with whom he shares his name

With Ballabriggs' National he too gained Aintree _____

Successive Fighting Fifths in ten and 11

All hurdles wins for Peddlers Cross equalled _____

SIMPLE SUMS

33.

Begin with the age that Waldgeist was when he won the Prix de l'Arc de Triomphe

Multiply by the number of races won by Dancing Brave

Divide by the number of times Sir Michael Stoute had been champion flat trainer up to and including his victory in 2009

Subtract the number of times that Islington won the Yorkshire Oaks

What is the number you have arrived at?

Is it:

A.   The number of times Whisper won the Ryanair Stayers' Hurdle?

B.   The number of times Iris's Gift won the Ryanair Stayers' Hurdle?

C.   The number of times Big Buck's won the Ryanair Stayers' Hurdle?

34.

Begin with the age that Tiger Roll was when he won his first Grand National

Multiply by the number of furlongs run in the Richmond Stakes at Goodwood

Divide by the number of times Persian Punch won the Jockey Club Cup

Subtract the number of Group One races normally run in a season at Newbury

What is the number you have arrived at?

Is it:

A.   The total number of races won by Ouija Board?

B.   The total number of races won by Enable?

C.   The total number of races won by Triptych?

FILL IN THE BLANKS

Can you fill in the ten blanks below? Each blank may be one word or the full name of a person, a horse or a race.

33.

The Grand National in _____ was won in a photo-finish by _____ from _____. It was a first win in the race for both trainer Paul Nicholls and jockey _____. The winner was the first grey horse to win since _____ in 1961. He had previously won three Grade One Chases, including two _____ in 2007 and 2008. _____ did better than any previous female rider in the race, by partnering _____ into third. Two former Grand National winners were in the field. The previous year's winner _____ finished sixth while the victor in 2009, _____, was pulled up.

34.

The _____-year-old _____, ridden by _____ and trained by Gordon Elliott, won the Melling Chase at Aintree in _____. For the winner, it was the third of what were to be six Grade One wins for him. The last of these and also his final appearance on a racecourse was in the following year's _____. His winning margin at Aintree was 26 lengths, from _____, who had been second in the race in 2013 to _____. In third place was _____, winner of the Paddy Power Gold Cup in 2013. The winner of the Paddy Power Gold Cup in 2012, _____, was in fifth, while the winner of the Queen Mother Champion Chase in 2014, _____, fell at the sixth.

GET IT IN ONE? OR TWO, OR THREE, OR FOUR?

How few clues do you need to identify these famous jockeys?

33.

Born 1981 in Ardrahan, County Galway, he served an apprenticeship with Jim Bolger.

He was Champion Conditional jockey for the 2004-05 season.

His first Cheltenham Festival win was in the Fred Winter Juvenile Novices' Handicap Hurdle on Shamayoun in 2006.

He won five Grade Ones on Cue Card.

34.

He was born in born in Stirling, Scotland.

He was chairman of Swindon Town FC from 2001 until August 2007.

There were 15 years between his first Epsom Derby winner and his last.

He co-presented horse racing on BBC1 until the end of the 2012 season.

WHERE'S THE LOGIC?

33.

The mare Fairy Godmother was having a successful season so far, winning her first four races, all of which had different sponsors – the one sponsored by the brewery being the biggest prize. She won four in a row, each time on different going – good, good to soft, soft and heavy – and with a different winning margin.

Her second win was by a neck. The third win was sponsored by a finance company; this wasn't the time she won by two lengths in soft going.

The first win was not the one sponsored by a TV channel. When the bookmaker was the sponsor, the going was heavy. Her fourth win, in good to soft, was not the win by five lengths.

In which sponsor's race did she win by ten lengths?

34.

The fifth running of the Cornham Cup had just taken place. Each year had seen a different horse win. They were, in alphabetical order, Lapis Lazuli, Moonstone, Morganite, Sapphire and Topaz. Each was ridden by a different jockey – Allen, Boyne, Cook, Driver and Eastwood – and each had a different trainer – Matthews, Nolan, Osborne, Price and Rawcliffe.

The jockey who rode Moonstone for Nolan did so a year after Allen rode the winner. The jockey who won the year before Allen won was riding for Matthews. Either Allen or Cook rode Lapis Lazuli but neither rode for Price.

In the second year Eastwood won but not on Topaz. The first winner was Morganite and was not ridden by Driver, who rode for Osborne.

Which jockey rode Topaz to win?

TELL ME THE ANSWER AND I'LL TELL YOU THE QUESTION

In each set of two questions and two answers below, only one of the answers is correct for only one of the questions. Can you find the matching pair?

33.

Questions

Which Prix de l'Arc de Triomphe winner was the first to be sired by Danehill?

Which Prix de l'Arc de Triomphe winner was the first to be sired by Galileo?

Answers

Dylan Thomas

Treve

34.

Questions

Which Berkshire racecourse opened in the 18th century?

Which Berkshire racecourse opened in the 19th century?

Answers

Windsor

Newbury

35.

Questions

Which jockey rode his first Eclipse Stakes winner on a horse trained by William Haggas?

Which jockey rode his first Eclipse Stakes winner on a horse trained by Roger Charlton?

Answers

Paul Hanagan

Tom Queally

36.

Questions

Which jockey rode Wayward Lad to the first of his three wins in the King George VI Chase in 1982?

Which jockey rode Wayward Lad to the last of his three wins in the King George VI Chase in 1985?

Answers

Robert Earnshaw

Graham Bradley

SIMPLE SUMS

35.

Begin with the number of letters in the name of the winner of the 2020 Dewhurst Stakes

Add the number of Group Ones normally run in a season at Newmarket

Divide by the number of times Ruby Walsh rode the winner of the Champion Hurdle

Subtract the number of times Un De Sceaux won the Queen Mother Champion Chase

What is the number you have arrived at?

Is it:

A.   The age of Stradivarius when he won his first Ascot Gold Cup?

B.   The age of Stradivarius when he won his second Ascot Gold Cup?

C.   The age of Stradivarius when he won his third Ascot Gold Cup?

36.

Begin with the number of times My Tent Or Yours finished second in the Champion Hurdle

Multiply by the number of letters in the name of the winner of the 2015 Irish Derby

Subtract the number of Epsom Derby winners sired by Cape Cross

Divide by the number of 2,000 Guineas winners ridden by Kieren Fallon

What is the number you have arrived at?

Is it:

A.   The number of letters in the name of the winner of the Coronation Cup in 2017?

B.   The number of letters in the name of the winner of the Coronation Cup in 2018?

C.   The number of letters in the name of the winner of the Coronation Cup in 2019?

FILL IN THE BLANKS

Can you fill in the ten blanks below? Each blank may be one word or the full name of a person, a horse or a race.

35.

In the _____ at Doncaster in 2017, Saxon Warrior won, beating Roaring Lion by a neck. This was the only time these two horses met as two-year-olds. Saxon Warrior was to meet Roaring Lion again, in five of his _____ outings as a three-year-old. In the _____, Saxon Warrior was ridden by _____ and won, with Roaring Lion back in fifth. The _____-trained colt did better in the _____, finishing third with Saxon Warrior in fourth. Roaring Lion won on their remaining three encounters. In both the Eclipse Stakes and the _____, he won by a _____ from Saxon Warrior in second. In between those two races, Roaring Lion won the Juddmonte International with his _____-trained rival back in _____.

36.

The _____ in 2012 was won by Somersby, ridden by _____. He was trained by _____ and subsequently by Mick Channon. It was to be his only Grade One win, but by the end of his career he had been runner-up in Grade Ones on _____ occasions, including _____ in the Queen Mother Champion Chase. He ran at _____ consecutive Cheltenham Festivals where, apart from the Queen Mother Champion Chase, he was placed in the _____ and the _____. Second at Ascot was _____, winner of the Queen Mother Champion Chase in 2012, with _____, winner of the Supreme Novices' Hurdle in 2011, in third.

GET IT IN ONE? OR TWO, OR THREE, OR FOUR?

How few clues do you need to identify these famous jockeys?

35.

Born in 1971, he grew up in Tamworth in Staffordshire.

He won the Oaks in 2008 on Ralph Beckett's Look Here.

His last domestic ride was at Newmarket in August 2015.

He shared the Flat Jockeys Championship in 2007.

36.

Born in Cambridge in 1988, his mother Jacqui was a trainer.

He has ridden the winner of at least one QIPCO British Champions Series race every year since 2013 to 2019.

He is 5ft 9in.

He won two races on the same horse at Royal Ascot in 2020.

WHERE'S THE LOGIC?

35.

There was a three-horse race between Baltimore, Chicago and Denver. Number two on the race card was a filly. The gelding won. Chicago was second. Denver was not the colt. Number one on the race card finished third.

What was the name of the gelding?

36.

The Clerk of the Course at Cornham was pleased with the number of runners in the first four races; there were 17, 18, 19 or 20 in each race. Particularly pleasing was the good turnout for the nursery race. Each of the races was over a different distance, the shortest of which was five furlongs.

The fourth race was a handicap for three-year-olds and above. The opener was over six furlongs but it was not the handicap for four-year-olds and above with 19 runners. The third race was not the maiden for three-year-olds over seven furlongs. The mile race attracted 17 runners. The second race on the card did not have 18 runners.

Which type of race had 18 runners?

TIME FOR A RHYME

Can you complete the missing rhymes in the poems below and identify the trainer that the poem is about?

33.

To be the champion soon is his greatest wish
To ride a winner, skipped an exam in _____
The farmers' son from Somerset has shot to fame
Not least for wins on Politologue and _____

34.

First to win the National and Cheltenham's big four
Nineteen hundred and twenty was his final _____
He says since his teens he had been like a coiled spring
He won his first Gold Cup on Tom Taaffe's _____

35.

From first rides in the 90s he was quick to learn
His first Champion Hurdle he won from _____
Won Cheltenham's Dawn Run on Willie Mullins's mare
And a second Champion Hurdle on _____

36.

A first professional win in 2002
Then three Irish champion titles he did _____
To two Grand National wins Tiger Roll he did steer
And had two Festival wins on _____

SIMPLE SUMS

37.

Begin with the number of British Racecourses that begin with the letters 'Che'

Multiply by the number of Group One races that are named after racehorses

Add the number of times Anak Pekan won the Chester Cup

Subtract the number of times Bristol De Mai won the Betfair Chase, up to and including 2020

What is the number you have arrived at?

Is it:

A.   The age of See You Then when he won his first Champion Hurdle?
B.   The age of See You Then when he won his second Champion Hurdle?
C.   The age of See You Then when he won his third Champion Hurdle?

38.

Begin with the number of Enable's consecutive wins as a three, four and five-year-old

Multiply by the number of times that Excelebration was second to Frankel

Subtract the number of races won by Eclipse

Divide by the maximum number of runners allowed in each Shergar Cup race

What is the number you have arrived at?

Is it:

A.   The number of racecourses in Surrey?
B.   The number of racecourses in North Yorkshire?
C.   The number of racecourses in Somerset?

FILL IN THE BLANKS

Can you fill in the ten blanks below? Each blank may be one word or the full name of a person, a horse or a race.

37.

The 2010 _____ saw the runner-up in the Epsom Oaks of 2009, _____, ridden by _____, beat the winner of the Epsom Oaks in 2010, _____, ridden by _____, into second place. However, neither of them started _____. That was _____ at 85-40 who had beaten the winner by a _____ in the Epsom Oaks. On this occasion she refused to race. The first and second filled the same places in the following year's _____ at Goodwood, in which the winner was being successful for the _____ year in a row.

38.

_____ won the British Champions Sprint at Ascot in _____, beating a field in which more than half of the runners were past or future Group One winners. Brando (third) and Signs of Blessing (fourth) are both winners of the Prix Maurice de Gheest at _____. Unplaced were _____ and _____, who went on to win this race in 2017 and 2019 respectively, dual _____ winner Mecca's Angel and Shalaa, winner at two of the Prix Morny and the _____. Also unplaced were _____ winners Quiet Reflection (2016) and Twilight Son (2015) – the former also won the Commonwealth Cup (2016) and the latter the Diamond Jubilee Stakes (2016). The winner himself went on to win the Diamond Jubilee Stakes in _____ and the Sprint Cup in _____.

GET IT IN ONE? OR TWO, OR THREE, OR FOUR?

How few clues do you need to identify these famous racehorses?

37.

This National Hunt star was sired by the King George VI and Queen Elizabeth Stakes winner King's Theatre.

He ran at seven consecutive Cheltenham Festivals.

He had the first of his nine Grade Two wins in a bumper at Aintree, by a length and a quarter from a horse who was to finish in front of him in three Champion Hurdles.

Perhaps his best run was when finishing a badly hampered third in 2014 Champion Hurdle.

38.

He began his career with two races in France, trained by Guillaume Macaire.

He won on his first six starts for Willie Mullins.

He won a Grade One in each of three visits to the Cheltenham Festival.

He was beaten a head by Cue Card in the 2015 King George VI Chase.

WHERE'S THE LOGIC?

37.

Four friends gathered to watch the racing on TV in the afternoon. They each had a different type of bet: a Trixie, a Patent, a Yankee and the other one just had each-way bets on individual races. By the end of the racing, one of them had won well, one had made a slight profit, one had made a slight loss and one had lost everything staked. Chris had a Patent. Jude was the one who only drank coffee. The wine drinker was not Jaimie. The one who drank only beer did worst. The one who stuck to drinking tea had a Trixie and was not the big winner. The each-way gambler showed a slight profit and wasn't the wine drinker. Alex lost but only a little.

Who did best with their bet?

38.

There had been a tight finish to the Jump Jockey Championship. The winner was just one ahead of the second, who was three in front of the third, who was one in front of the fourth, with the fifth just a further three behind. The youngest of the five was aged 22 and the others were 24, 30, 32 and 36.

The 22-year-old was not fourth. Ashton didn't win. Bradshaw was one behind the 24-year-old but in front of Carter. The jockey next to Earnshaw in age finished one behind Earnshaw. Only one jockey was older than Dunphy and it was not Bradshaw.

How old was Carter?

TELL ME THE ANSWER AND I'LL TELL YOU THE QUESTION

In each set of two questions and two answers below, only one of the answers is correct for only one of the questions. Can you find the matching pair?

37.

Questions

What is the number of complete furlongs in the cup race traditionally run at York's Ebor Festival?

What is the number of complete furlongs in the cup race traditionally run on British Champions Day?

Answers

16

17

38.

Questions

Who rode Champagne Fever, trained by Willie Mullins, to victory in the Champion Bumper at Cheltenham?

Who rode Relegate, trained by Willie Mullins, to victory in the Champion Bumper at Cheltenham?

Answers

Ruby Walsh

Katie Walsh

39.

Questions

Which jockey rode their only Epsom Derby winner in 1996?

Which jockey rode their only Epsom Derby winner in 1997?

Answers

Willie Ryan

Olivier Peslier

40.

Questions

Which horse was the first six-year-old to win the Arkle Challenge Trophy after 2000?

Which horse was the first seven-year-old to win the Arkle Challenge Trophy after 2000?

Answers

Well Chief

Azertyuiop

SIMPLE SUMS

39.

Begin with the age that Royal Rebel was when he won his first Ascot Gold Cup

Multiply by the number of three-year-old fillies who have won the Prix de l'Arc de Triomphe in the 21st century up to and including 2020

Divide by the number of racecourses in West Yorkshire

Subtract by the number of times Big Orange won the Goodwood Cup

What is the number you have arrived at?

Is it:

A.   The age of Istabraq when he won his first Champion Hurdle?

B.   The age of Istabraq when he won his second Champion Hurdle?

C.   The age of Istabraq when he won his third Champion Hurdle?

40.

Begin with the number of Betfair Chases won by Kauto Star

Multiply by the number of furlongs in the Ormonde Stakes at Chester

Subtract the number of times that Tony McCoy was champion jump jockey

Divide by the number of hurdles jumped in the Champion Hurdle

What is the number you have arrived at?

Is it:

A.   The number of Ascot Gold Cups won by Yeats?

B.   The number of Ascot Gold Cups won by Sagaro?

C.   The number of Ascot Gold Cups won by Royal Rebel?

FILL IN THE BLANKS

Can you fill in the ten blanks below? Each blank may be one word or the full name of a person, a horse or a race.

39.

The winner of the _____ at Aintree in 2017 was _____, who won by a neck from Cue Card. The winner was a second Grade One Chase success for jockey _____, after the combination took the _____ at Kempton in 2015. As well as the second, the winner had two other multiple winners of the Betfair Chase behind: _____, winner of the Haydock race in 2012 and _____, who was last of the six finishers; and _____, who would win the first of his Betfair Chases later in the year, finished fifth. The other finishers were _____, a Hennessy Gold Cup winner, in third, and in fourth _____, whose best performance was a second in Frodon's 2019 _____.

40.

The 1,000 Guineas in _____ was won by _____ at 9-1 from her stablemate _____, the 5-4 favourite. It was a _____ Classic winner for jockey Wayne Lordan. The winning trainer, _____, had won the race in the previous year with _____. The winner won her next two races, the _____ and then the _____ at Royal Ascot. Later in the season, the runner-up won the Prix de l'Opéra from _____, another stablemate unplaced in the 1,000 Guineas. The runner-up's last win was as a four-year-old in the _____at Newbury.

GET IT IN ONE? OR TWO, OR THREE, OR FOUR?

How few clues do you need to identify these famous racehorses?

39.

He won his only point-to-point race at Summerhill in Ireland in record time.

He was pulled up on his last two appearances, in the Hennessy Gold Cup and in the Grand National.

He was owned by a partnership that shared their name with a 1990s BBC drama series.

He won on five out of eight chase appearances at Cheltenham.

40.

He won the first of his 55 hurdle races – a novices' hurdle at Newbury – by a distance.

He had two wins and two thirds in the Grade Two Holloway's Hurdle at Ascot.

He was twice winner of the Grade Two National Spirit Hurdle at Fontwell.

His only Grade One success was in the Long Walk Hurdle where he made all to win by nine lengths with dual Champion Hurdle winner Hardy Eustace in second.

WHERE'S THE LOGIC?

39.

The chief executive welcomed the other five members of the team to the most recent meeting at Cornham racecourse. They were seated at a round table and each person had a member of the opposite sex on either side. Each was having a different drink.

The operations manager sat with Samuel on her left and Adrian on her right. The black coffee drinker sat in between Lucy and Harriet whilst Rachel, the clerk of the course, drank orange juice. The head of marketing sat in between Rachel and the head of finance. The tea drinker sat to the left of the catering manager. Before business began, Harriet held up her espresso and jokingly said to Adrian, opposite, who drank cappuccino, 'Under Starters' Orders?' Daniel laughed. Who drank water? Who was the chief executive?

40.

The first six horses in the finish flashed past the winning post in a tight bunch. After the photo finish, it was clear that Bravado had not won and that Domingo was not last. Domingo was at least two places behind Bravado, and Caligula was as many places in front of Alcatraz as Bravado was in front of Domingo. The number of Farrago's place was twice the number of Excess's place. Caligula was not fourth and Alcatraz was not last. There were no dead heats.
Can you work out the finishing order of the six?

TIME FOR A RHYME

Can you complete the missing rhymes in the poems below and identify the horse that the poem is about?

37.

Ridden in nine Grade One wins by Paddy or Joe
With his superb jumping he could put on a _____
Won the Champion Bumper at 40-1
A Betfair fourth, a second and three that he _____

38.

Noel Fehily was most often on board when he won
Thirty-six runs of which seven wins at _____
Two King George wins ensured his everlasting fame
At Kempton they have a steeplechase in his _____

39.

When aged 12 he came back to Leopardstown once more
And took his Hennessy Gold Cups total to _____
At the Cheltenham Festival his wins were double
His Gold Cup best was second to _____

40.

The jockey as so often was Tony McCoy
For a Champion Hurdle success from _____
When aged 11 he made another headline
With an Irish Champion Hurdle win in _____

SOLUTIONS

SIMPLE SUMS

1.

Begin with the number of times Frankel won the Sussex Stakes (2011, 2012)   2

Multiply by the number of letters in the name of the 2019 Epsom Derby winner (Anthony Van Dyck)   x 14 = 28

Add the number of times Johnny Murtagh rode the winner of the King George VI and Queen Elizabeth Stakes (2003, 2007, 2008, 2013)   + 4 = 32

Divide by the number of furlongs run in the Falmouth Stakes   ÷ 8 = 4

A   Desert Orchid won the King George VI Chase four times (1986, 1988-90). Wayward Lad won three (1982, 1983, 1985) and Silviniaco Conti won two (2013, 2014).

2.

Begin with the number of times Red Rum ran in the Grand National (1973-77)   5

Multiply by the number of times Faugheen won the Christmas Hurdle (2014, 2015)   x 2 = 10

Add the number of times Gordon Richards was champion flat jockey (1925, 1927-29, 1931-40, 1942-53)   + 26 = 36

Divide by the number of letters in the name of the 2020 2,000 Guineas winner. (Kameko)   ÷ 6 = 6

C   Sole Power's first win in the King's Stand Stakes was when he was six (2013). Blue Point first won the race aged four (2018), Equiano when he was three (2008).

3.

Begin with the number of consecutive races won by Sprinter Sacre in his winning run which began in December 2011   10

Add the number of letters in the name of the 2016 winner of the 2,000 Guineas (Galileo Gold)   + 11 = 21

Subtract the number of letters in the name of the 2016 winner of the 1,000 Guineas (Minding)   - 7 = 14

Divide by the number of times Joseph O' Brien rode the winner of the Epsom Derby (2012, 2014)   ÷ 2 = 7

C   Rock On Ruby was seven when he won the Champion Hurdle (2012), Rooster Booster was nine (2003) and Annie Power was eight (2016).

4.

Begin with the number of times Lester Piggott rode the winner of the St Leger (1960-61, 1967-68, 1970-72, 1984)   8

Multiply by the number of times St Nicholas Abbey won the Coronation Cup (2011-13)   x 3 = 24

Add the number of times John Francome was outright jump champion jockey (1975-76, 1978-79, 1980-81, 1982-83, 1983-84, 1984-85)   + 6 = 30

Divide by the number of Group One races normally run in a season at York (International Stakes, Yorkshire Oaks, Nunthorpe Stakes)   ÷ 3 = 10

C   Don Cossack won the Cheltenham Gold Cup in 2016, Lord Windermere in 2014 and Coneygree in 2015.

5.

Begin with the number of times Blue Point won the King's Stand Stakes (2018, 2019)   2

Add the number of Grade Ones won by Hurricane Fly   + 22 = 24

Multiply by the number of racecourses in Cumbria (Carlisle, Cartmel)   x 2 = 48

Divide by the number of hurdles jumped in the Long Walk Hurdle   ÷ 12 = 4

A   Barry Geraghty rode the winner of the Champion Hurdle four times (2009, 2014, 2018, 2020), Tony McCoy three times (1997, 2006, 2010) and Noel Fehily two times (2012, 2017)

6.

Begin with the number of fences jumped in the Tingle Creek Chase   13

Add the age that Addeybb was when he won the 2020 Champion Stakes   + 6 = 19

Multiply by the number of times Warsaan won the Coronation Cup (2003, 2004)   x 2 = 38

Subtract the number of consecutive races won by Winx   - 33 = 5

C   Further Flight won the Jockey Club Cup five times (1991-95). He won the Doncaster Cup once (1992) and the Goodwood Cup two times (1991, 1992).

7.

Begin with the number of times that Cue Card won the Betfair Chase (2013, 2015, 2016)   3

Multiply by the number of times Richard Dunwoody was champion jumps jockey (1992-93, 1993-94, 1994-95)   x 3 = 9

Add the number of different fences jumped in the Grand National   + 16 = 25

Subtract the number of races won by Secretariat   - 16 = 9

C   Arkle was nine when he won his third consecutive Cheltenham Gold Cup in 1966.

8.

Begin with the number of Group Ones won by Winx   25

Multiply by the number of times Sprinter Sacre won the Queen Mother Champion Chase (2013, 2016)   x 2 = 50

Divide by the number of lengths by which Shergar won the Epsom Derby   ÷ 10 = 5

Subtract the number of consecutive years that Richard Johnson was champion jump jockey starting with the 2015-16 season   - 4 = 1

B   The Sprint Cup is the only Group One normally run at Haydock. Goodwood has three Group Ones – the Goodwood Cup, the Sussex Stakes and the Nassau Stakes – whilst Doncaster has two – the St Leger and the Vertem Futurity Stakes

9.

Begin with the age that Master Minded was when he won his first Tingle Creek Chase (2008)   5

Add the number of races won by the unbeaten Ribot   + 16 = 21

Multiply by the number of racecourses in Norfolk (Fakenham and Great Yarmouth)   x 2 = 42

Divide by the number of complete furlongs run in the Queen Alexandra Stakes   ÷ 21 = 2

A   Kingsgate Native was two when he won the Nunthorpe Stakes in 2007. Mozart won aged three in 2001 and Marsha was four when she won in 2017.

10.

Begin with the number of letters in the name of the 2020 St Leger winner (Galileo Chrome)   13

Multiply by the number of finishers in the 2001 Grand National   x 4 = 52

Subtract the number of Epsom Oaks winners trained by Henry Cecil (1985, 1988, 1989, 1996, 1997, 1999, 2000, 2007)   - 8 = 44

Divide by the number of times Lester Piggott was champion flat jockey (1960, 1964-71, 1981-82)   ÷ 11 = 4

A   Big Buck's won the Stayers' Hurdle Chase four times (2009-12). Inglis Drever won three (2005, 2007, 2008) and Baracouda won two (2002, 2003).

11.

Begin with the number of times Willie Carson rode the winner of the Epsom Derby (1979, 1980, 1989, 1994)   4

Multiply by the number of times Khalid Abdullah owned the winner of the Prix de l'Arc de Triomphe (1985, 1986, 2006, 2010, 2017, 2018)   x 6 = 24

Divide by the number of furlongs in the Lockinge Stakes   ÷ 8 = 3

Add the number of Group One races normally run in a season at Epsom (The Derby, The Oaks, Coronation Cup)   + 3 = 6

A   Kieren Fallon was Champion Jockey six times (1997-99, 2001-03); Pat Eddery 11 times (1974-77, 1986, 1988-91, 1993, 1996) and Richard Hughes three times (2012-14).

12.

Begin with the number of times Andre Fabre had trained the winner of the Prix de l'Arc de Triomphe up to and including Waldgeist in 2019 (1987, 1992, 1994, 1997, 1998, 2005, 2006, 2019)   8

Multiply by the number of times Kauto Star won the King George VI Chase (2006-09, 2011)   x 5 = 40

Subtract the number of races in Altior's unbeaten run which began in October 2015   - 19 = 21

Divide by the number of winners ridden by Frankie Dettori at Ascot on 28 September 1996   ÷ 7 = 3

A   Pat Eddery rode three winners of the 2,000 Guineas (1983, 1984, 1993), Lester Piggott five (1957, 1968, 1970, 1985, 1992) and Willie Carson four (1972, 1980, 1987, 1989).

13.

Begin with the number of furlongs in the Cambridgeshire Handicap   9

Multiply by the number of letters in the name of the 2018 winner of the Epsom Derby (Masar)   x 5 = 45

Subtract the number of fences jumped in the Ryanair Chase   - 17 = 28

Divide by the number of consecutive years that Paul Nicholls was champion jump trainer starting in the 2005-06 season   ÷ 7 = 4

B   Aidan O'Brien trained four English Classic winners in 2017 (2,000 Guineas, 1,000 Guineas, Derby, St Leger), two in 2016 (1,000 Guineas, Oaks) and three in 2018 (2,000 Guineas, Oaks, St Leger).

14.

Begin with the age that Neptune Collonges was when he won the Grand National   11

Add the number of furlongs run in the Goodwood Cup   + 16 = 27

Divide by the number of times Pat Eddery rode the winner of the Epsom Derby (1975, 1982, 1990)   ÷ 3 = 9

Subtract the number of times Hurricane Fly won the Champion Hurdle (2011, 2013)   - 2 = 7

B   Rock of Gibraltar won seven consecutive Group Ones; Frankel nine and Black Caviar eight.

15.

Begin with the number of races in Stradivarius's unbeaten run which began in May 2018   10

Multiply by the number of times that Frankie Dettori was champion flat jockey in the 1990s (1994, 1995)   x 2 = 20

Subtract the number of times Master Minded won the Queen Mother Champion Chase (2008, 2009)   - 2 = 18

Divide by the number of fillies who won the St Leger between 1945 and 2000 (1955 Meld, 1959 Cantelo, 1977 Dunfermline, 1983 Sun Princess, 1985 Oh So Sharp, 1992 User Friendly)   ÷ 6 = 3

A   Badsworth Boy won the Queen Mother Champion Chase three times (1983-85), Moscow Flyer won two times (2003, 2005) and Sire De Grugy won once (2014).

16.

Begin with the number of times that Yeats won the Goodwood Cup   2

Multiply by the number of complete furlongs in the Lonsdale Cup at York   x 16 = 32

Divide by the number of Epsom Derby winners sired by Montjeu (2005 Motivator, 2007 Authorised, 2011 Pour Moi, 2012 Camelot)   ÷ 4 = 8

Subtract the number of racecourses in Nottinghamshire (Nottingham, Southwell)   - 2 =6

B   Kauto Star won his first King George VI Chase aged six, his first Ascot Chase in 2008 aged eight and his first Cheltenham Gold Cup aged seven in 2007.

17.

Begin with the number of letters in the name of the Aidan O' Brien-trained 2002 Epsom Derby winner (High Chaparral)   13

Multiply by the number of times Enable won the Yorkshire Oaks   x 2 = 26

Add the number of times Hardy Eustace won the Champion Hurdle (2004, 2005)   + 2 = 28

Divide by the number of races won by Frankel   ÷ 14 = 2

A   Warwickshire has two racecourses: Stratford-on-Avon and Warwick. Berkshire has three: Ascot, Newbury and Windsor. Shropshire has one: Ludlow.

18.

Begin with the age that Best Mate was when he won his first Cheltenham Gold Cup (2002)   7

Multiply by the number of times Stradivarius had won the Ascot Gold Cup up to and including his 2020 victory (2018-20)   x 3 = 21

Divide by the number of times Willie Carson rode the winner of the St Leger (1977, 1983, 1988)   ÷ 3 = 7

Add the number of letters in the name of the 2020 British Champions Long Distance Cup winner (Trueshan)   + 8 = 15

A   Black Caviar won 15 Group One races, Frankel ten and Goldikova 14.

19.

Begin with the number of times Martin Pipe was champion jump trainer (1988-89, 1992-93, 1995-96, 2004-05)   15

Multiply by the number of times Best Mate won the King George VI Chase (2002)   x 1 = 15

Add the number of Group Ones normally run in a season at Sandown Park (The Eclipse Stakes)   + 1 = 16

Divide by the number of times that Dahlia won the King George VI and Queen Elizabeth Stakes (1973, 1974)   ÷ 2 = 8

B   Anapurna won the Epsom Oaks in 2019, Forever Together in 2018 and Love in 2020.

20.

Begin with the number of times Brigadier Gerard won the Champion Stakes (1971, 1972)   2

Multiply by the number of stones Hoof It carried to victory in the 2011 Stewards' Cup   x 10 = 20

Add the number of furlongs in the Victoria Cup   + 7 = 27

Divide by the number of times Steve Cauthen was champion flat jockey (1984, 1985, 1987)   ÷ 3 = 9

C   Synchronised was nine when he won the Cheltenham Gold Cup in 2012; Kicking King seven in 2005 and Looks Like Trouble eight in 2000.

21.

Begin with the number of times Persian War won the Champion Hurdle (1968-70)   3

Multiply by the number of winners ridden by Holly Doyle at Windsor on 29 August 2020   x 5 = 15

Add the number of fences jumped before the Foinavon in the Grand National   +6 =21

Subtract the number of complete furlongs run in the Cesarewitch Handicap   - 18 = 3

C   Un De Sceaux won the Clarence House Chase three times (2016-18), Master Minded two times (2009, 2011) and Sire De Grugy once (2014).

22.

Begin with the number of letters in the name of the winner of the 2018 King George VI Chase (Clan Des Obeaux)   13

Multiply by the number of racecourses in Merseyside (Aintree, Haydock Park)   x 2 = 26

Subtract the age that Notnowcato was when he won the Eclipse Stakes (2007)   - 5 = 21

Divide by the number of times that See You Then won the Champion Hurdle (1985-87)   ÷ 3 = 7

B   Latrobe won the Irish Derby in 2018, Capri in 2017 and Sovereign in 2019.

23.

Begin with the number of hurdles jumped in the Ballymore Novices' Hurdle   10

Add the number of furlongs run in the July Cup   + 6 = 16

Divide by the number of times Bronze Angel won the Cambridgeshire Handicap (2012, 2014)   ÷ 2 = 8

Subtract the number of times Frankie Dettori rode the winner of the Oaks up to and including 2020 (1994, 1995, 2002, 2017, 2019)   - 5 = 3

B   Al Eile won the Aintree Hurdle three times (2005, 2007, 2008), Oscar Whisky twice (2011, 2012) and The New One once (2014).

24.

Begin with the number of stones carried to victory by Burrough Hill Lad in the 1984 Hennessy Cognac Gold Cup   12

Add the number of times Kieren Fallon rode the winner of the Epsom Derby (1999, 2003, 2004)   + 3 = 15

Multiply by the number of times See More Business won the King George VI Chase (1997, 1999)   x 2 = 30

Divide by the number of stones carried to victory by Cloth Cap in the 2020 Ladbrokes Trophy   ÷ 10 = 3

A   Reve De Sivola won the Long Walk Hurdle three times up to and including 2020 (2012-14), Paisley Park two times (2018, 2020) and Thistlecrack once (2015).

25.

Begin with the age that Cirrus des Aigles was when he won the Champion Stakes (2011)   5

Multiply by the number of times Denman finished second in the Cheltenham Gold Cup (2009-11)   x 3 = 15

Add the number of letters in the name of the winner of the 2020 Charlie Hall Chase (Cyrname)   + 7 = 22

Divide by the number of times Lester Piggott rode the winner of the Ascot Gold Cup 1957, 1958, 1961, 1963, 1965, 1975-77, 1979, 1981, 1982)   ÷ 11 = 2

A   John Oxx trained two Epsom Derby winners (2000, 2009), Dick Hern three (1970, 1980, 1989) and Henry Cecil four (1985, 1987, 1993, 1999).

26.

Begin with the number of letters in the name of the 2015 2,000 Guineas winner (Gleneagles)   10

Multiply by the number of times Double Trigger won the Doncaster Cup (1995, 1996, 1998)   x 3 = 30

Divide by the number of times Frankie Dettori had won the Prix de l'Arc de Triomphe after Enable's second win (1995, 2001, 2002, 2015, 2017, 2018)   ÷ 6 = 5

Subtract the number of racecourses in Devon (Exeter, Newton Abbot)   - 2 = 3

A   Nijinsky won the 2,000 Guineas, the Epsom Derby and the St Leger in 1970; Sea the Stars won the 2,000 Guineas and the Epsom Derby in 2009 and Galileo won the Epsom Derby in 2001.

27.

Begin with the number of times that Lester Piggott rode the winner of the Epsom Derby (1954, 1957, 1960, 1968, 1970, 1972, 1976, 1977, 1983)   9

Multiply by the number of times that Swain won the King George VI and Queen Elizabeth Stakes (1997, 1998)   x 2 = 18

Subtract the number of times that Istabraq won the Champion Hurdle (1998-2000)   - 3 = 15

Add the number of times that Peter Scudamore was champion jump jockey outright (1985-86, 1991-92)   + 7 = 22

B   22 fences are jumped in the Cheltenham Gold Cup, 18 in the King George VI Chase and 19 in the Betfair Chase.

28.

Begin with the age that Treve was when she won her second Prix de l'Arc de Triomphe (2014)   4

Multiply by the number of times that Sole Power won the King's Stand Stakes (2013, 2014)   x 2 = 8

Add the number of times Golden Miller won the Cheltenham Gold Cup (1932-36)   + 5 = 13

Subtract the number of hurdles jumped in the Stayers' Hurdle   -12 = 1

C   John Dunlop was champion flat trainer once (1995), Peter Walwyn twice (1974, 1975) and Dick Hern three times (1962, 1972, 1980).

29.

Begin with the number of letters in the name of the 2020 winner of the Arkle Challenge Trophy (Put The Kettle On)   14

Multiply by the number of times Silviniaco Conti won the Betfair Chase (2012, 2014)   x 2 = 28

Subtract the number of times Vinnie Roe won the Irish St Leger (2001-04)   - 4 = 24

Divide by the number of consecutive years that Aidan O' Brien was Champion Flat trainer starting with the 2007 season   ÷ 2 = 12

A   Amberleigh House was 12 when he won the Grand National in 2004, Red Marauder 11 in 2001 and Don't Push It ten in 2010.

30.

Begin with the age that Faugheen was when he won the Champion Hurdle (2015)   7

Add the number of times that Sadler's Wells was champion sire in GB and Ireland (1990, 1992-2004)   + 14 = 21

Multiply by the number of finishers in the 1928 Grand National   x 2 = 42

Divide by the number of times Quevega won the David Nicholson Mares' Hurdle (2009-14)   ÷ 6 = 7

C   Hors La Loi III was seven when he won the Champion Hurdle in 2002, Katchit was five (2008) and Punjabi six (2009).

31.

Begin with the age that Yeats was when he won his fourth Ascot Gold Cup (2009)   8

Multiply by the number of times Aaim To Prosper won the Cesarewitch Handicap (2010, 2012)   x 2 = 16

Divide by the number of times Baracouda won the Long Walk Hurdle (2000, 2001, 2003, 2004)   ÷ 4 = 4

Add the number of runners in the Epsom Derby won by Camelot   +9 = 13

C   Moscow Flyer won 13 Grade One races, Apple's Jade 11 and Kauto Star 16.

32.

Begin with the number of races won by the unbeaten Lammtarra   4

Add the number of times Willie Carson was champion flat jockey (1972, 1973, 1978, 1980, 1983)   + 5 = 9

Subtract the number of letters in the name of the winner of the 2020 Paddy Power Gold Cup (Coole Cody)   - 9 = 0

Add the number of Epsom Derby winners sired by Sadler's Wells (Galileo 2001, High Chaparral 2002)   +2 = 2

B   Kauto Star won the Tingle Creek Chase two times (2005, 2006), Sprinter Sacre once (2012) and Flagship Uberalles three times (1999-2001).

33.

Begin with the age that Waldgeist was when he won the Prix de l'Arc de Triomphe (2019)   5

Multiply by the number of races won by Dancing Brave   x 8 = 40

Divide by the number of times Sir Michael Stoute had been champion flat trainer up to and including his victory in 2009 (1981, 1986, 1989, 1994, 1997, 2000, 2003, 2005, 2006, 2009)   ÷ 10 = 4

Subtract the number of times that Islington won the Yorkshire Oaks (2002, 2003)   - 2 = 2

A   Whisper won the Ryanair Stayers' Hurdle twice (2014, 2015), Iris's Gift (2004) once and Big Buck's four times (2009-2012).

34.

Begin with the age that Tiger Roll was when he won his first Grand National (2018)   8

Multiply by the number of furlongs run in the Richmond Stakes at Goodwood   x 6 = 48

Divide by the number of times Persian Punch won the Jockey Club Cup (2000, 2002, 2003)   ÷ 3 = 16

Subtract the number of Group One races normally run in a season at Newbury (Lockinge Stakes)   - 1= 15

B   Enable won a total of 15 races, Ouija Board won ten and Triptych won 14.

35.

Begin with the number of letters in the name of the winner of the 2020 Dewhurst Stakes (St Mark's Basilica)   15

Add the number of Group Ones normally run in a season at Newmarket (2,000 Guineas, 1,000 Guineas, Falmouth Stakes, July Cup, Cheveley Park Stakes, Middle Park Stakes, Sun Chariot Stakes, Fillies' Mile, Dewhurst Stakes)   + 9 = 24

Divide by the number of times Ruby Walsh rode the winner of the Champion Hurdle (2011, 2013, 2015, 2016)   ÷ 4 = 6

Subtract the number of times Un De Sceaux won the Queen Mother Champion Chase   - 0 = 6

C   Stradivarius was six when he won his third consecutive Ascot Gold Cup in 2020.

36.

Begin with the number of times My Tent Or Yours finished second in the Champion Hurdle (2014, 2016, 2017)   3

Multiply by the number of letters in the name of the winner of the 2015 Irish Derby (Jack Hobbs)   x 9 = 27

Subtract the number of Epsom Derby winners sired by Cape Cross (Sea The Stars 2009, Golden Horn 2015)   - 2 = 25

Divide by the number of 2,000 Guineas winners ridden by Kieren Fallon (2000, 2001, 2005, 2006, 2014)   ÷ 5 = 5

C   Defoe won the Coronation Cup in 2019, Cracksman in 2018 and Highland Reel in 2017.

37.

Begin with the number of British Racecourses that begin with the letters 'Che' (Chelmsford, Cheltenham, Chepstow, Chester)   4

Multiply by the number of Group One races that are named after racehorses (The Eclipse Stakes, The Sun Chariot Stakes)   x 2 = 8

Add the number of times Anak Pekan won the Chester Cup (2004, 2005)   + 2 = 10

Subtract the number of times Bristol De Mai won the Betfair Chase, up to and including 2020 (2017, 2018, 2020)   - 3 = 7

C   See You Then was seven when he won his third consecutive Champion Hurdle in 1987.

38.

Begin with the number of Enable's consecutive wins as a three, four and five-year-old   12

Multiply by the number of times that Excelebration was second to Frankel (2011 - Greenham Stakes and Queen Elizabeth II Stakes, 2012 - Lockinge Stakes and Queen Anne Stakes)   x 4 = 48

Subtract the number of races won by Eclipse   - 18 = 30

Divide by the maximum number of runners allowed in each Shergar Cup race   ÷ 10 = 3

C   Somerset has three racecourses: Bath, Taunton and Wincanton. Surrey has four: Epsom Downs, Kempton Park, Lingfield Park and Sandown Park. North Yorkshire has five: Catterick, Redcar, Ripon, Thirsk and York.

39.

Begin with the age that Royal Rebel was when he won his first Ascot Gold Cup (2001)   5

Multiply by the number of three-year-old fillies who have won the Prix de l'Arc de Triomphe in the 21st century up to and including 2020 (2008, 2011, 2013, 2017)   x 4 = 20

Divide by the number of racecourses in West Yorkshire (Pontefract, Wetherby)   ÷ 2 = 10

Subtract by the number of times Big Orange won the Goodwood Cup (2015, 2016)   - 2 = 8

C   Istabraq was eight when he won his third consecutive Champion Hurdle in 2000.

40.

Begin with the number of Betfair Chases won by Kauto Star   4
(2006, 2007, 2009, 2011)

Multiply by the number of furlongs in the Ormonde Stakes at Chester   x 13 = 52

Subtract the number of times that Tony McCoy was champion jump jockey (1995-96, 2014-15)   - 20 = 32

Divide by the number of hurdles jumped in the Champion Hurdle   ÷ 8 = 4

A   Yeats won four Ascot Gold Cups (2006-09). Sagaro won three (1975-77) and Royal Rebel won two (2001-02).

FILL IN THE BLANKS

1.

The field for the 2016 running of the **Queen Mother Champion Chase** at the Cheltenham Festival included the three most recent winners of the race, **Dodging Bullets**, **Sire De Grugy** and **Sprinter Sacre**. However, none of them were favourite; that was Un De Sceaux who finished second to **Sprinter Sacre** in a famous victory. In third place was **Special Tiara** who went on to win the race the following year. The winner was ridden by **Nico de Boinville** and trained by **Nicky Henderson**. The winner had just one more race – the **Celebration Chase** at Sandown, winning once again from Un De Sceaux, but by the bigger margin of **15** lengths.

2.

Night of Thunder won the 2,000 Guineas in **2014** by half a length from **Kingman**. This was the only race in which the runner-up was defeated – his subsequent Group One wins that season included the Irish 2,000 Guineas and the **St James's Palace Stakes** at Royal Ascot. Third behind Night of Thunder was **Australia**, who went on to win both the Epsom Derby and the **Irish Derby** in June as well as the **Juddmonte International Stakes** at York in August. Eighth in the 2,000 Guineas was the 2014 winner of the **Doncaster St Leger**, Kingston Hill. The horse who finished tenth behind Night of Thunder, **The Grey Gatsby,** won two Group Ones later in the season – the **Prix du Jockey Club** at Chantilly and the **Irish Champion Stakes**.

3.

The winner of the 2016 **Triumph Hurdle** was Ivanovich Gorbatov, whose trainer, **Aidan O' Brien**, is better known for his successes on the flat and whose son, **Joseph Patrick**, later took over the training of the horse. Second was **Apple's Jade** who in her next race, the Anniversary Four-year-old Novices' Hurdle at **Aintree**, reversed placings with the winner and beat him by 41 lengths in the first of what was to become her **11** Grade One successes. The third, **Footpad**, was back at the Cheltenham Festival with a win two years later in the Arkle Challenge Trophy Chase. It is unlikely that anyone would have predicted that two of the unplaced horses – who were stablemates – would go on to win three consecutive **King George VI Chases** between them. They were **Clan Des Obeaux** in sixth and **Frodon** in eighth.

4.

Was won the **Oaks** at Epsom in 2012, with a starting price of **20-1**. Trained by **Aidan O'Brien**, it was a first British Classic winner for jockey **Seamie Heffernan**. In six subsequent starts, the winner failed to win again. The second horse, **Shirocco Star**, also did not subsequently win a race, although later in 2012 she was **second** in the Irish Oaks. The beaten favourite in third place at Epsom, trained by **John Gosden**, was **The Fugue**, who went on to great success. She won Group One races as a three, four and five-year-old. These included the **Nassau Stakes** at Goodwood, the Yorkshire Oaks and the **Prince of Wales's Stakes** at Royal Ascot.

5.

The Champion Stakes in **2014** was won by **Noble Mission**, whose full brother, **Frankel**, had won the race two years previously. Both were by Galileo out of **Kind**. This was the winner's third Group One success that season, following victories in the **Tattersalls Gold Cup** in Ireland and the **Grand Prix de Saint-Cloud** in France. He was ridden in all three wins by **James Doyle**. In second place, beaten a **neck**, was Al Kazeem who himself was a winner of the **Tattersalls Gold Cup** at the Curragh in 2013 and 2015. In fifth place was the horse who won the race three years before, **Cirrus des Aigles**.

6.

The Ryanair Chase at Cheltenham in **2009** was won by **Imperial Commander**, ridden by **Paddy Brennan** and trained by Nigel Twiston-Davies. The winner had already won the Paddy Power Gold Cup at Cheltenham and would go on to win the 2010 **Gold Cup** at the Festival. He beat the odds-on favourite, **Voy Por Ustedes**, by two lengths. The second had already won four Grade One Chases including both the **Arkle Challenge Trophy Chase** in 2006 and the **Queen Mother Champion Chase** in 2007 at the Cheltenham Festival. Back in sixth was **Monet's Garden**, a horse who later had the **Old Roan Chase** at Aintree renamed after him, following his **three** wins in the race.

7.

The **Sussex Stakes** in **2019** was won by Too Darn Hot. This was his last appearance on a racecourse and his third Group One win, following his previous race, the Prix Jean Prat at **Deauville** and, as two-year-old, the **Dewhurst Stakes** at Newmarket. At the end of his first season, he won the Cartier Award for Champion Two-year-old Colt. At Goodwood, he beat **Circus Maximus** into second place, reversing his defeat by that colt in the **St James's Palace Stakes** at Royal Ascot. In sixth place at Goodwood was **Phoenix of Spain**, who had beaten Too Darn Hot into second place in the Irish 2,000 Guineas. Too Darn Hot was trained by John Gosden and ridden in all of his races by **Frankie Dettori**, carrying the pink with a **grey** sash colours of Lord Lloyd-Webber. He started favourite or joint favourite in each of his **nine** races.

8.

The King George VI Chase in **2018** was won by the **six**-year-old **Clan Des Obeaux**. He was ridden by **Harry Cobden** and trained by **Paul Nicholls** for whom this was a tenth win in the race. He won from Thistlecrack and **Native River**, winner of that year's Cheltenham Gold Cup. Another Gold Cup winner, **Coneygree**, who had won in 2015, unseated his rider. The winner's stablemate, **Politologue**, was ridden by **Sam Twiston-Davies** and finished fourth, whilst the favourite, **Might Bite**, second in that year's Cheltenham Gold Cup, was last of the seven finishers.

9.

The Arkle Challenge Trophy Chase in **2014** was won by **Western Warhorse**, trained by **David Pipe** and ridden by **Tom Scudamore**. He started at odds of 33-1 in what was only his **second** outing over fences. His next race, the Manifesto Novices' Chase at **Aintree**, in which he finished third to Uxizandre, proved to be his last. In fourth place at Cheltenham was **Dodging Bullets** who went on to great success in the following season, winning three Grade Ones. These were the Tingle Creek Chase at **Sandown**, the **Clarence House Chase** at Ascot and the Queen Mother Champion Chase. In last place behind the shock winner was **Rock On Ruby**, who had won the Champion Hurdle two years previously, in 2012.

10.

Danedream won the 2011 **Prix de l'Arc de Triomphe** by **five** lengths at odds of 20-1. She broke the course record and became only the second filly to win the race in the 21st century. In third was another filly, **Snow Fairy,** who had completed the double of the **Epsom Oaks** and the Irish Oaks in the previous year. Fourth was **So You Think**, who had won the **Eclipse Stakes** at Sandown and the Irish Champion Stakes earlier in the season. The winner went on to win the King George VI and Queen Elizabeth Stakes the following year, by a **nose** from **Nathaniel**, with **Aidan O'Brien**-trained St Nicholas Abbey in third.

11.

The Irish Derby in **2001** was won by the 4-11 favourite, **Galileo**. It was the second win in the race for his trainer, **Aidan O' Brien**, and the first for his jockey, **Michael Kinane**. The horse in third place, **Golan**, had been runner-up to the winner in the Epsom Derby and had earlier won the **2,000 Guineas** at Newmarket. In seventh place, at 66-1, was **Vinnie Roe**, who later that season had the first of four consecutive wins in the **Irish St Leger**. What was to be the winner's final success came in his next race, the **King George VI and Queen Elizabeth Stakes**, which he won by two lengths from Fantastic Light. Subsequently, the winner became best known for his exceptional success as a **sire**.

12.

Honeysuckle, ridden by Rachael Blackmore, won the **David Nicholson Mares' Hurdle** at the Cheltenham Festival in 2020. She had won all **eight** of her previous starts. These included the Hatton's Grace Hurdle at **Fairyhouse** and the Irish Champion Hurdle at **Leopardstown**, both Grade Ones. The Cheltenham race was the first time since her racecourse debut when she did not start **favourite**. The winner in 2018, **Benie Des Dieux**, ridden by **Paul Townend,** started odds-on favourite and finished second, half a length behind the winner; in 2019 she fell at the last with the race at her mercy, leaving **Roksana**, who was **fourth** in 2020, to win.

13.

Denman was the winner of the Cheltenham Gold Cup in **2008**, in the first of what were to be **four** appearances in the race. For the winner's trainer, **Paul Nicholls**, it was a third win in the race. The second horse, **Kauto Star**, who started odds-on favourite, was having his second of what were to be **six** runs in the race. Between them, they won the race **three** times. The horse in third, **Neptune Collonges**, was having the second of four tilts at the race; he was never closer than **third** but the last race of his career was to be his greatest success, when he won the 2012 **Grand National** by a nose.

14.

None of the first three in the betting for the Champion Hurdle in **2019** finished in the first three. The favourite, **Apple's Jade**, gave a below-par performance to finish sixth. The second favourite at 5-2, **Laurina**, came fourth. The third favourite, **Buveur D'Air** at 11-4, fell at the **third** hurdle. The race was won by **Espoir D'Allen** with Mark Walsh riding in the familiar emerald green with yellow hoops of

JP McManus. His winning margin of **15** lengths was a record for the race. For the second horse, **Melon**, it was the **third** consecutive year of finishing second at the Cheltenham Festival. It was the winner's last race as he had to be put down following a freak accident in the following August.

15.

Circus Maximus won the **Queen Anne Stakes** in 2020. The race was the first Group One race at the **Royal Ascot** meeting. He won by a head from the **John Gosden**-trained Terebellum. Further back in the field were the 2018 winner of the race, **Accidental Agent**, and the winner of the 2018 1,000 Guineas, **Billesdon Brook**. It was the winner's third Group One success, following the **St James's Palace Stakes** at the same meeting the year before and the Prix du Moulin de Longchamp. The winner's **final** racecourse appearance, later that year, was when he was a **neck** second to stable companion Order of Australia in the **Breeders' Cup Mile**.

16.

Cue Card won the Betfair Chase in **2013**. It was the first of his five attempts in the race, which resulted in three wins, one **second** and one **fourth**. In third place was Silviniaco Conti, who also ran five times in the race, resulting in two wins, in **2012** and **2014**. Two Cheltenham Gold Cup winners were out of the first three: **Long Run**, winner in 2011, and **Bobs Worth**, who started favourite for this, his first race since winning the Gold Cup earlier in the year. Another top-class chaser out of the frame was Silviniaco Conti's stablemate **Tidal Bay**, who had his Cheltenham Festival win five years earlier in the **Arkle Challenge Trophy Chase**.

17.

The **Juddmonte International** Stakes in 2015, run over **ten** and a half furlongs at **York**, was won by **Arabian Queen** at 50-1 by a neck from the 4-9 favourite, **Golden Horn**, ridden by **Frankie Dettori**. The Grey Gatsby was third. The winner was ridden by **Sylvestre de Sousa**, for whom it was a first win in the race. For the winning trainer, **David Elsworth**, it was a second win, having won it previously in 1990 with **In the Groove**. It was the first of two defeats that season for the beaten favourite; he was later second to **Found** in the Breeders' Cup Turf.

18.

The **Charlie Hall Chase** at Wetherby in 2016 was won by **Irish Cavalier**, ridden by Jonathan Moore and trained by **Rebecca Curtis**. It was the highest grade race that the horse won. The previous year's winner, **Cue Card**, was third. In second place was the winner from two years before, **Menorah**, who was notable for being a four times winner (2014-17) of the **Oaksey Chase** at Sandown. He had also won the **Supreme Novices' Hurdle** at the Cheltenham Festival in 2010. Back in fourth was **Blaklion**, the winner earlier in the year of the **RSA Chase** at the Cheltenham Festival, who six months later would finish fourth in the Grand National to **One For Arthur**.

19.

The Epsom Derby in **2017** was won by **Wings of Eagles**, who was ridden by **Padraig Beggy** and started at 40-1. In second place was the winner's stablemate, Cliffs of Moher. In third was **Cracksman** who went on to win the Champion Stakes that season and again the following season. Another stable companion was **Capri**, in sixth, who went on to Group One wins in that season's **Irish Derby** and **Doncaster St. Leger**. The high quality of the field was also in evidence in Benbatl who finished fifth, and Best Solution, who finished eighth, as both went on to win Group Ones. **Rekindling**, who beat only **two** horses home, won the **Melbourne Cup** at Flemington later that year.

20.

The World Hurdle at the Cheltenham Festival in **2006** was unusual because of the presence amongst the riders of a top-class jockey from the flat – **Johnny Murtagh**. He rode **Golden Cross**, who was beaten a head into second place by **My Way De Solzen**. The winner returned to the Festival the following year to take the **Arkle Challenge Trophy Chase**. On his eventual return to hurdling, he contested the World Hurdle again in 2008 but could finish only fifth behind **Inglis Drever**, who was winning it for the **third** time. Fifth in 2006 was **Baracouda**, who was having his fifth and final run in the race, following two seconds and two wins in **2002** and **2003**, when the race was known as the Stayers' Hurdle.

21.

Capri, the winner of the St Leger in **2017**, subsequently won only one more race, a Group Three. However, the next four horses home all went on to great success. The second, **Crystal Ocean**, won the Prince of Wales's Stakes as a five-year-old and was twice beaten by a neck in the **King George VI and Queen Elizabeth Stakes**. **John Gosden** trained both the third, **Stradivarius**, who was unbeaten in the following season and became the leading stayer in Britain, and the fifth, **Coronet**, who won two Group Ones in **France** as a five-year-old. Fourth was **Rekindling**, trained by **Joseph Patrick O'Brien**, who on his next run won the Melbourne Cup.

22.

The **Fighting Fifth Hurdle** in 2015 was won by Identity Thief, trained by **Henry De Bromhead**. Later in the season he was sixth in the Champion Hurdle behind **Annie Power**, while his only other Grade One success was to come in the Ryanair Stayers' Hurdle at **Aintree** in 2018. He beat Top Notch by a neck at Newcastle and ten lengths away in third was **Wicklow Brave**, a talented performer under both rules who, in the following year, won the **Irish St Leger** from the 1-7 favourite Order of St George and seven months later the **Punchestown Champion Hurdle** from My Tent Or Yours. Sixth at Newcastle was **Irving**, who had won the race in **2014** and was to take it again in **2016**.

23.

The Nunthorpe Stakes at York in **2015** was won by Mecca's Angel, ridden by **Michael Dods**, who would ride her on her second victory in the race in **2016**. In second place was the 13-8 favourite, **Acapulco**, trained in the USA by **Wesley A. Ward**. Out of the placings were no less than three past and future winners of the King's Stand Stakes at Royal Ascot. In fourth place was **Sole Power**, winner of the King's Stand Stakes in 2013 and 2014, as well as the Nunthorpe Stakes in **2010** and 2014. In fifth was **Goldream**, who won the King's Stand Stakes in his race before the Nunthorpe and won the **Prix de L'Abbaye de Longchamp** on his next appearance. In tenth place, at 20-1, was **Profitable**, who went on to victory in the Royal Ascot sprint the following year.

24.

The **Long Walk Hurdle** at Ascot in 2020 was won by **Paisley Park**, ridden by **Aidan Coleman**, by a **neck** from Thyme Hill. In doing so, he reversed the placings from when the pair previously met in the Long Distance Hurdle at **Newbury** just 22 days earlier where he finished second, beaten one and a half lengths. For the winner, it was a **third** Grade One success, the first having been in this race **two** years previously. Third was **Roksana**, who had won the David Nicholson Mares' Hurdle at the Cheltenham Festival in 2019. In sixth place was the 2019 winner of the race, **The Worlds End**, while last of the seven finishers was **Main Fact**, who had won his previous nine races, all in handicap company.

25.

The winner of the **King George VI and Queen Elizabeth Stakes** in 2010 was **Harbinger**. Trained by **Sir Michael Stoute** and ridden by Olivier Peslier, he won by 11 lengths and in a course record time. In second place was Cape Blanco, who on his previous outing had won the **Irish Derby** and on his next outing won the **Irish Champion Stakes**. In third place was **Youmzain**, who had finished second in each of the last three runnings of the **Prix de l'Arc de Triomphe**. The winner's stable companion, **Workforce**, started odds-on favourite but could only finish **fifth**. The race was to be the winner's last. Just **two** weeks after his victory he suffered a fractured leg on the gallops and was retired.

26.

The **2007** Eclipse Stakes was won by **Notnowcato**. The winning jockey, **Ryan Moore**, made a daring manoeuvre by taking the winner alone up the stands' side of the course and he rode another **three** winners on the card. He won by a length and a half from Authorized, ridden by **Frankie Dettori**, who on his previous outing had won the **Epsom Derby** by **five** lengths. In third place was **George Washington**, who had won the previous season's 2,000 Guineas. The second had his revenge on the winner later in the season when he won the **Juddmonte International Stakes** at York, with the Eclipse winner in **third** place.

27.

The **Supreme Novices Hurdle** in 2015 was won by **Douvan** from Shaneshill. The winning trainer, **Willie Mullins**, was winning the race for the **third** consecutive year. For the winner, this was the third in a winning sequence of **13** since joining Willie Mullins (eight of which were Grade Ones), which came to an end in the Queen Mother Champion Chase **two** years later. For the third horse, **Sizing John**, this was one of seven occasions when he was placed behind the winner. He came into his own, however, in 2017, when he won four Grade One chases – the **Irish Gold Cup**, the **Cheltenham Gold Cup**, the **Punchestown Gold Cup** and the John Durkan Memorial Punchestown Chase.

28.

The **seven**-year-old **Many Clouds** won the **Hennessy Gold Cup Chase** at Newbury in **2014**. Ridden by **Leighton Aspell**, he won by three-and-a-quarter lengths from Houblon Des Obeaux. Fourth was the winner of the Welsh Grand National in January 2013, **Monbeg Dude**. Favourite was the five-year-old **Djakadam**, trained by Willie

Mullins. He finished eighth and would go on to be second twice in the Cheltenham Gold Cup, first to **Coneygree** in 2015 and then to **Don Cossack** in 2016. The winner went on to win the **Grand National** later that season at 25-1 by one-and-three-quarter lengths from Saint Are. He subsequently had a race at Aintree named after him.

29.

The 2016 **Ascot Gold Cup** was won by **Order of St George**, ridden by **Ryan Moore.** This was the first of his three appearances in the race. In 2017 he was beaten a short head by **Big Orange**; in 2018, on his last racecourse appearance, he was **fourth** to Stradivarius. Later in 2016 he finished third in the Prix de l'Arc de Triomphe behind his stable companions **Found** and **Highland Reel**. He returned in the following year to finish **fourth** behind **Enable.** He also won the **Irish St Leger** in 2015 and 2017.

30.

Presenting Percy was an impressive winner of the **RSA Chase** in 2018 at the Cheltenham Festival. Ridden by **Davy Russell**, he won by seven lengths from Monalee. The horse in third place later that year started 3-1 favourite and won the Welsh Grand National with the Cheltenham fourth, **Ballyoptic**, back in sixth. This pair were to meet again in the 2019 **Charlie Hall Chase** at Wetherby where it was **Ballyoptic**'s turn to win, beating **Elegant Escape** by **three**-and-three-quarter lengths. The runner at Cheltenham who had the greatest subsequent success was **Al Boum Photo** who fell two out. He won his first **Cheltenham Gold Cup** at the Festival the following year.

31.

The Irish St Leger in 2014 was won by the **six**-year-old **Brown Panther**. It was the winner's second attempt in the race following a third place to **Royal Diamond** in 2012. Trained by **Tom Dascombe** and ridden by **Richard Kingscote**, the winner won by six and a half lengths and a **head** from two previous Doncaster St Leger winners – **Leading Light**, who had won the English Classic in the previous year, and **Encke**, the winner in 2012. The winner's other big successes included the Group Two **Goodwood Cup** in 2013 and the **Dubai Gold Cup** in 2015.

32.

The seven-runner field for the 2016 Dewhurst Stakes included some horses who were to be top-class performers over the next three seasons. For the winner, **Churchill**, it was the second of **four** consecutive Group One wins – the next two were the

2017 **2,000 Guineas** and the **Irish 2,000 Guineas**. The third, **Blue Point**, went on to win the King's Stand Stakes at Royal Ascot in 2018 and both that race and the Diamond Jubilee Stakes at the 2019 Royal Ascot meeting. Also carrying the **Godolphin** colours, **Thunder Snow**, in fourth, became the first horse to win two **Dubai World Cups**, in 2018 and 2019. Lancaster Bomber in second won the **Tattersalls Gold Cup** in 2018, whilst Rivet Delight in fifth won the **Racing Post Trophy** on his next start.

33.

The Grand National in **2012** was won in a photo-finish by **Neptune Collonges** from **Sunnyhillboy**. It was a first win in the race for both trainer Paul Nicholls and jockey **Daryl Jacob**. The winner was the first grey horse to win since **Nicolaus Silver** in 1961. He had previously won three Grade One Chases, including two **Punchestown Gold Cups** in 2007 and 2008. **Katie Walsh** did better than any previous female rider in the race, by partnering **Seabass** into third. Two former Grand National winners were in the field. The previous year's winner **Ballabriggs** finished sixth while the victor in 2009, **Mon Mome**, was pulled up.

34.

The **eight**-year-old **Don Cossack**, ridden by **Tony McCoy** and trained by Gordon Elliott, won the Melling Chase at Aintree in **2015**. For the winner, it was the third of what were to be six Grade One wins for him. The last of these and also his final appearance on a racecourse was in the following year's **Cheltenham Gold Cup**. His winning margin at Aintree was 26 lengths, from **Cue Card**, who had been second in the race in 2013 to **Sprinter Sacre**. In third place was **John's Spirit**, winner of the Paddy Power Gold Cup in 2013. The winner of the Paddy Power Gold Cup in 2012, **Al Ferof**, was in fifth, while the winner of the Queen Mother Champion Chase in 2014, **Sire de Grugy**, fell at the sixth.

35.

In the **Racing Post Trophy Stakes** at Doncaster in 2017, Saxon Warrior won, beating Roaring Lion by a neck. This was the first time these two horses met as two-year-olds. Saxon Warrior was to meet Roaring Lion again, in five of his **six** outings as a three-year-old. In the **2,000 Guineas**, Saxon Warrior was ridden by **Donnacha O'Brien** and won, with Roaring Lion back in fifth. The **John Gosden**-trained colt did better in the **Epsom Derby**, finishing third with Saxon Warrior in fourth. Roaring Lion won on their remaining three encounters. In both the Eclipse Stakes and the **Irish Champion Stakes**, he won by a **neck** from Saxon Warrior in second. In between those two races, Roaring Lion won the Juddmonte International with his **Aidan O' Brien**-trained rival back in **fourth**.

36.

The **Clarence House Chase** in 2012 was won by Somersby, ridden by **Dominic Elsworth**. He was trained by **Henrietta Knight** and subsequently by Mick Channon. It was to be his only Grade One win, but by the end of his career he had been runner-up in Grade Ones on **six** occasions, including **twice** in the Queen Mother Champion Chase. He ran at **eight** consecutive Cheltenham Festivals where, apart from the Queen Mother Champion Chase, he was placed in the **Supreme Novices' Hurdle** and the **Arkle Challenge Trophy Chase**. Second at Ascot was **Finian's Rainbow**, winner of the Queen Mother Champion Chase in 2012, with **Al Ferof**, winner of the Supreme Novices' Hurdle in 2011, in third.

37.

The 2010 **Yorkshire Oaks** saw the runner-up in the Epsom Oaks of 2009, **Midday**, ridden by **Tom Queally**, beat the winner of the Epsom Oaks in 2010, **Snow Fairy**, ridden by **Richard Hughes**, into second place. However, neither of them started **favourite**. That was **Sariska** at 85-40 who had beaten the winner by a **head** in the Epsom Oaks. On this occasion she refused to race. The first and second filled the same places in the following year's **Nassau Stakes** at Goodwood, in which the winner was being successful for the **third** year in a row.

38.

The Tin Man won the British Champions Sprint at Ascot in **2016**, beating a field in which more than half of the runners were past or future Group One winners. Brando (third) and Signs of Blessing (fourth) are both winners of the Prix Maurice de Gheest at **Deauville**. Unplaced were **Librisa Breeze** and **Donjuan Triumphant**, who went on to win this race in 2017 and 2019 respectively, dual **Nunthorpe Stakes** winner Mecca's Angel and Shalaa, winner at two of the Prix Morny and the **Middle Park Stakes**. Also unplaced were **Sprint Cup** winners Quiet Reflection (2016) and Twilight Son (2015) – the former also won the Commonwealth Cup (2016) and the latter the Diamond Jubilee Stakes (2016). The winner himself went on to win the Diamond Jubilee Stakes in **2017** and the Sprint Cup in **2018**.

39.

The winner of the **Betway Bowl** at Aintree in 2017 was **Tea For Two**, who won by a neck from Cue Card. The winner was a second Grade One Chase success for jockey **Lizzie Kelly**, after the combination took the **Kauto Star Novice Chase** at Kempton in 2015. As well as the second, the winner had two other multiple winners of the Betfair Chase behind: **Silviniaco Conti**, winner of the Haydock race in 2012 and **2014**, who was last of the six finishers; and **Bristol de Mai**, who would win the first of his Betfair Chases later in the year, finished fifth. The other finishers were **Smad Place**, a Hennessy Gold Cup winner, in third, and in fourth **Aso**, whose best performance was a second in Frodon's 2019 **Ryanair Chase**.

40.

The 1,000 Guineas in **2017** was won by **Winter** at 9-1 from her stablemate **Rhododendron**, the 5-4 favourite. It was a **first** Classic winner for jockey Wayne Lordan. The winning trainer, **Aidan O' Brien**, had won the race in the previous year with **Minding**. The winner won her next two races, the **Irish 1,000 Guineas** and then the **Coronation Stakes** at Royal Ascot. Later in the season, the runner-up won the Prix de l'Opéra from **Hydrangea**, another stablemate unplaced in the 1,000 Guineas. The runner-up's last win was as a four-year-old in the **Lockinge Stakes** at Newbury.

GET IT IN ONE? OR TWO, OR THREE, OR FOUR?

1.
Cracksman

He had Stradivarius in fourth in his first race. His 2017 win in the Champion Stakes was the first Group One win in Europe for the offspring of Frankel. Only Twice Over (2009-10) had won consecutive Champion Stakes this century before Cracksman in 2017 and 2018.

2.
Magical

Magical is by Galileo out of Halfway to Heaven. She was ridden by Ryan Moore, Seamie Hefferman, Wayne Lordan and Donnacha O'Brien. She was second to Enable in the 2018 Breeders' Cup Turf and in the following season's Eclipse Stakes and Yorkshire Oaks.

3.
Islington

Islington was by Sadler's Wells out of Hellenic. In the Yorkshire Oaks of 2002, Kazzia was fourth; in the 2003 race, Casual Look was seventh of eight.

4.
Dar Re Mi

She won the Pretty Polly Stakes and Yorkshire Oaks in 2009 and the Dubai Sheema Classic the following year. She was disqualified and placed fifth in the 2009 Prix Vermeille. Her fifth foal was Too Darn Hot.

5.
Charlie Appleby

He became trainer for Godolphin in 2013 and trained Masar to win the Epsom Derby in 2018; this was also his first Classic winner. He trained Cross Counter to win the Melbourne Cup in 2018.

6.
Richard Fahey

His father was an engineer who worked around the world. He trained the Godolphin-owned Ribchester to win Group Ones in the Prix Jacques Le Marois, the Lockinge

Stakes, the Prix du Moulin and the Queen Anne at Royal Ascot, where he broke the course record.

7.
Mark Johnston

Mark Johnston began training in Lincolnshire and his first year with a licence yielded a single winner. He moved to Middleham in 1988. He became Britain's winning-most trainer when the Frankie Dettori-ridden Poet's Society won at York's Ebor meeting in 2018. It was his 4,194th British winner, surpassing Richard Hannon Sr's tally. He trained Attraction to win five Group Ones including the 2004 1,000 Guineas.

8.
Rebecca Curtis

Teaforthree won the National Hunt Chase in 2012 for this Pembrokeshire-based trainer and was third to Auroras Encore in the 2013 Grand National.

9.
Jimmy Fortune

He rode more than 1,800 winners in Britain. His last ride was a third on Nathra in the Sun Chariot Stakes at Newmarket in October 2017.

10.
Richard Johnson

Anzum won the Stayers' Hurdle at 40-1 in 1999. Richard Johnson was 16-times runner-up to Tony McCoy in the Jump Jockey Championship before his first win in 2016.

11.
Brian Hughes

He was Champion Conditional jockey in 2007-08 and British jump racing champion jockey in 2019-20 with 141 winners.

12.
Peter Scudamore

Peter Scudamore's father Michael won the Grand National on Oxo in 1959 and his son Tom is a successful jump jockey. He won the Champion Hurdle on Celtic Shot (1988) and Granville Again (1993) and the Queen Mother Champion Chase on Pearlyman (1987). He was champion jump jockey eight times (including one win shared with John Francome). He also set the record for most winners in a season (221) in 1988-89. He retired aged 34.

13.
Farhh

He sired Dee Ex Bee who was second in the Derby, Ascot Gold Cup, Goodwood Cup and Lonsdale Cup. He was second to Frankel in 2012 in the Sussex Stakes and the Juddmonte International.

14.
Rock of Gibraltar

In winning seven consecutive Group Ones in 2001-02, he broke the record that had stood for 31 years – the six consecutive Group Ones won by Mill Reef.

15.
The Giant Bolster

His second, fourth and third in the Cheltenham Gold Cup came in 2012, 2013 and 2014. In all he made 15 appearances at Cheltenham, winning three times.

16.
Overturn

Overturn's sire was Barathea. He was the first-ever horse to complete the double of winning Newcastle's Northumberland Plate and the Fighting Fifth Hurdle, in 2010 and 2011 respectively. He was second to Ile de Re, also trained by Donald McCain, in the 2012 Chester Cup and second in the Champion Hurdle in 2012 to Rock On Ruby.

17.
Henrietta Knight

She trained Best Mate, who won three consecutive Cheltenham Gold Cups (2002-04) amongst his six Grade Ones. She trained Edredon Bleu to win the Peterborough Chase in 1998, 1999, 2000 and 2001 and Best Mate to win it in 2002.

18.
Michael Dickinson

In the UK, he is perhaps best known for training the first five in the 1983 Cheltenham Gold Cup: Bregawn, Captain John, Wayward Lad, Silver Buck and Ashley House. He was Champion Jumps Trainer for three consecutive seasons starting in 1981-82. In the USA he is perhaps best known for training Da Hoss to win the 1996 and 1998 Breeders' Cup Mile despite the horse only having had one race in between, owing to injury.

19.
Alan King

His big Cheltenham Festival wins include the World Hurdle with My Way de Solzen, the Queen Mother Champion Chase with Voy Por Ustedes, the Champion Hurdle with Katchit and the Ryanair Chase with Uxizandre.

20.
Michael Stoute

Sir Michael Ronald Stoute (born 22 October 1945 in Barbados) is a Barbadian British thoroughbred horse trainer in flat racing. He was knighted for services to sport and tourism in Barbados. He was champion flat trainer for the tenth time in 2009.

21
Aidan Coleman

Born in Innishannon, County Cork, Ireland, in 1988, Aidan Coleman's other big wins include the Arkle Challenge Trophy in 2020 and the Queen Mother Champion Chase in 2021 on Put The Kettle On.

22.
Daryl Jacob

His 2012 Grand National win was on Neptune Collonges. His four Scilly Isles Novices' Chase winners were Gitane Du Berlais (2015), Bristol De Mai (2016), Top Notch (2017) and Terrefort (2018). He won the Grande Course de Haies d'Auteuil on L'Ami Serge in 2017. He rode a five timer on 9 January 2021 at Wincanton.

23.
Jamie Moore

His siblings who are also jockeys are Ryan, Joshua over jumps and amateur jockey Hayley. Trainer Gary Moore is his father who himself is the son of Brighton trainer and car dealer Charlie Moore. His Scottish Grand National win was on Al Co.

24.
Sam Waley-Cohen

Born in 1982, Sam Waley-Cohen is perhaps the most successful Aintree rider of the modern era; his wins over the Grand National fences are: 2005 Foxhunters': Katarino; 2006 Foxhunters': Katarino; 2006 Topham: Liberthine; 2014 Foxhunters': Warne; 2014 Becher Chase: Oscar Time; 2015 Topham: Rajdhani Express.

25.
Dream Ahead

Dream Ahead ran nine times, winning on six occasions. Trained by David Simcock, he was Cartier Champion Sprinter of 2011.

26.
Sinndar

Sinndar retired after his win in the Prix de l'Arc de Triomphe in 2000. Youmzain, by Sinndar out of Sadima, was second in the Prix de l'Arc de Triomphe in 2007, 2008 and 2009.

27.
Hedgehunter

His three consecutive high-level seconds were in 2006. His Grand National win was in 2005.

28.
Denman

Denman was by Presenting, third in the Epsom Derby in 1995. After his Cheltenham Gold Cup win in 2008, his three seconds in the race were to Kauto Star (2009), Imperial Commander (2010) and Long Run (2011). It was in the Jim Brown Memorial Novices' Chase in 2006 that he beat Don't Push It.

29.
Barry Hills

Steve Cauthen's first Classic winner was Tap on Wood in the 2,000 Guineas in 1979. Barry Hills trained his 3,000th winner when Chapter And Verse won at Pontefract on 7 April 2009. All of his children were sons: John, Michael, Richard, Charles and George.

30.
Marco Botti

Marco Botti is the son of Alduino Botti. Sesmen won the Group Three Prestige Stakes and the stables are called Prestige Place.

31.
Jessica Harrington

She won the Champion Hurdle with Jezki, the Queen Mother Champion Chase with Moscow Flyer (twice) and the Cheltenham Gold Cup with Sizing John. Alpha Centauri won the 2018 Falmouth Stakes (and also the Irish 1,000 Guineas) and Millisle the 2019 Cheveley Park Stakes.

32.
Philip Hobbs

He also won the Triumph Hurdle and the Cesarewitch Handicap in 2006 with Detroit City and the Champion Hurdle in 2003 with Rooster Booster.

33.
Paddy Brennan

His five Grade Ones on Cue Card were the Betfair chase (twice), the King George VI Chase, the Ascot Chase and the Betway Bowl. He also won the Cheltenham Gold Cup on Imperial Commander in 2010.

34.
Willie Carson

He was born in 1942 and rode a total of 3,828 winners. Troy in 1979 was his first Epsom Derby winner followed by Henbit (1980), Nashwan (1989) and Erhaab (1994). His co-presenter on BBC1 racing was Clare Balding.

35.
Seb Sanders

Seb Sanders rode his first winner on Band On The Run at Pontefract in June 1990. His first Group One was in the July Cup in 1997 on 50-1 Compton Place. He shared the Flat Jockeys Championship with Jamie Spencer in 2007 after Spencer won the last race of the season.

36.
James Doyle

James Doyle's first winner was in June 2005 on Richard Price-trained Farnborough in a handicap at Wolverhampton. His first Classic win was in the Irish 2,000 Guineas on Kingsman and he won the Ascot Gold Cup on Big Orange in 2017. He has been retained by Godolphin since 2015. In 2020 he won the King's Stand Stakes and the Diamond Jubilee Stakes at Royal Ascot on Blue Point.

37.
The New One

Second to him in the bumper was My Tent Or Yours who had The New One behind him when second in the Champion Hurdles of 2014, 2016 and 2017.

38.
Vautour

His three Cheltenham Festival wins were the Supreme Novices' Hurdle in 2014, the JLT Novices' Chase in 2015 and the Ryanair Chase in 2016.

39.
Imperial Commander

His five chase wins at Cheltenham included the Ryanair Chase (2009) and the Cheltenham Gold Cup (2010). Apart from Cheltenham, he won at just two courses under rules – Newcastle and Haydock.

40.
Lough Derg

His wins in the National Spirit Hurdle were in 2008 and 2009. His Long Walk Hurdle win was in 2007.

WHERE'S THE LOGIC?

1.

Ashton's win on the 4-6 shot can only have been at Bowminster, meaning Carter rode the winner at Cornham. So Duplicity at 2-1 must have won at Armfield. The winner at Bowminster cannot be Euphoria or Duplicity so must be Fidelity, with Euphoria winning at Cornham.

2.

The £20 bet on the favourite was not placed with Bell, could not have been with Chamberlin (second favourite), nor with Chapman (£30) so it must have been with Weaver. The bet taken by Chamberlin must have been £10 and the one taken by Bell £50. Jude's bet on the fourth in the betting can't be with Weaver or Chamberlin and Chris bet with Bell so Jude must have bet with Chapman. Jamie's stake was not £10 so it must be the £20 with Weaver, meaning the horse backed by Chris must have been the third favourite and Alex must be the backer of the second favourite.

3.

The two miles four furlongs win at 5-2 is not Cornham and cannot be at Bowminster (two miles and two furlongs) or at Denley (2-1), so it must be at Armfield. The win at two miles on heavy can't be at Armfield (two miles four furlongs), Bowminster (two miles two furlongs) or Cornham (good) so it must be at Denley. The win at 6-1 on good to soft can't be at Armfield (5-2), Cornham (good) or Denley (heavy) so must it be at Bowminster. This leaves the two miles, six furlongs win at evens to be at Cornham and the win on soft to be at Armfield.

4.

The jockey wearing green sleeves with quarters is not drawn one and cannot be drawn two (red sleeves), nor three (hoops), so must be drawn four. The jockey wearing a red cap with blue sleeves cannot be drawn one (green cap), two (red sleeves) or four (green sleeves) so must be drawn three. Therefore, only the jockey drawn one can have yellow sleeves. The jockey with a diamond does not have yellow sleeves so must be in stall two. The jockey with a blue cap does not have a diamond so he must be on the horse drawn four. The jockey with red sleeves must have a yellow cap and the crossbelts can only belong to the jockey in stall one.

5.

The horse who won had a noseband and it was Bucolic or Carapace. Advance must have been second. Advance can't be in a noseband or blinkers so must have cheekpieces. Therefore, Carapace must have worn blinkers and finished third. Bucolic was first and in a noseband.

6.

The five-year-old grey is not with Osborne, nor with Matthews (who has the four-year-old), nor Nolan (who has the black horse) so must be with Price. Of the two-year-old and the three-year-old, one must be black with Nolan and the other with Osborne at Thornfield, so the brown at Twelve Oaks must be the four-year-old. The two-year-old is not bay so must be black and with Nolan. So, the three-year-old is the bay and is with Osborne at Thornfield Hall. The two-year-old is not at Manderley so the five-year-old must be there and the two-year-old is the black horse at Pemberley.

7.

The novice hurdle is not fourth. The novice hurdle is not second or third so must be first. The handicap hurdle must be second. As the handicap hurdle is immediately before the two-mile race, the two-mile race must be the third race. The two miles and four furlongs is not a hurdle race so must be the fourth race. For the handicap chase to come immediately after the three-mile chase it must be the third race and the three-mile race second.

So, the two miles and six furlongs novice hurdle must be the first race and the novice chase last.

8.

Because after the race in which she was pulled up Bradshaw rode her next, she could not be pulled up in the fourth and Bradshaw didn't ride her on her first outing. If the race in which she was brought down was next to the race in which she unseated her rider, that can only be the third or fourth race. So Bradshaw can't have ridden Mishap in the fourth outing, but Carter did. Carter wasn't unseated so must have ridden when she was brought down and she unseated her rider on her third outing. As there was a jockey who took the ride in-between Dunphy and Bradshaw, Bradshaw must have ridden on the third outing, Dunphy in the first and Ashton in the second. Mishap must have been pulled up in her second race so fell in her first, with Dunphy on board.

9.

There are only six different possible finishing orders for the first three horses, and the friends and the tipster have used five of them. In only two of the six possible orders of finishing can Boscobel be second – Chris has chosen one of them but no one chose the other. Therefore, the result can only have been Columbo from Boscobel and Artichoke (with Dumbo fourth).

10.

Neither Wordsworth, Eliot, Keats or Tennyson fell at the first, so that must have been Milton. Keats, trained by North and ridden by Dunphy, must have fallen at the fourth. So Tennyson must have fallen at the fifth and Eliot at the second. The horse ridden by Carter was trained by Parkes and can only be Wordsworth, so Milton must be ridden by Earnshaw and Eliot is trained by Quinn.

11.

Chopin was first, ridden by Rees, and Shubert was second. Wagner finished in between the mount of Stott and Schubert, so must be third, with the fourth ridden by Stott. Monteverdi can only be fourth if the mounts of Wilson and Owen are either side of him. The only way to have one jockey with the same first letter as their horse is if Wilson rides Wagner, and Owen rides Ravel in fifth place. Cullinan rode Schubert and Morgan rode Offenbach into last place.

12.

Matthews doesn't train Mars, Jupiter or Neptune so must train Venus. Osborne doesn't train Mars (red colours), Neptune (Price) or Venus (Matthews) so must train Jupiter. This leaves Nolan as the trainer of Mars. Osborne trains the third, and neither Matthews nor Price can train the fourth, so Nolan must train the fourth. Price's horse is not in yellow so must be in green and the winner, leaving Matthews in second place with Venus in yellow.

13.

The winning distance at Bowminster is a neck, with Honeydew it is five lengths; defeat by Pink Flamingo at Cornham was not by a head or three lengths so must be by two lengths. The defeat at Denley by Shocking Pink is not a head so can only be by three lengths. When What Larks was beaten by five lengths it was not at Armfield so the winning margin there must have been a head (and Easthill is the course where Honeydew won by five lengths). Aero Blue can't have won by a neck so that must have been Antique White.

So, Aero Blue won by a head, at Armfield.

14.

Aspect was not in the fourth, third (not 9-4) or the second race, so must have been in the first race and started at 6-4. Coral must be 9-4 and in the third race so Divine is in the second race and must be third. Coral must be second, which leaves Bauble coming last at 11-4.

15.

Merlin cannot have been fourth last time out (Tristan), or third, unplaced or a winner, so he must have been second. Merlin is aged either five or six. So, the horse who was unplaced last time out is four or five and the horse who was third last time out was either the six or seven-year-old. Only the eight-year-old can have won last time out (Merlin was second, Tristan fourth, the one who was third last time out was either six or seven years old and the one who was unplaced last time out was either four or five years old), and he must be Lancelot. Bedivere does not have cheekpieces, nor blinkers, or a hood or a visor, so must have a noseband. Also, Bedivere last time out didn't win, wasn't second, wasn't unplaced and wasn't fourth so must have been third, so Merlin is six. The five-year-old with a visor unplaced last time is Gawain.

Merlin had blinkers, Tristan is four and has cheekpieces.

16.

The black horse in stable one is not Cancel Culture, cannot be Influencer (stable two), or Fake News (grey), so must be Avatar. Influencer must be the bay and Cancel Culture must be brown. Pegasus is the sire of the horse in stable four which cannot be Avatar or Influencer and Cancel Culture was sired by Bucephalus so Pegasus must have sired Fake News, who is grey and in stable four. The only stable left for Cancel Culture is stable three.

Marengo is not the sire of the bay so must be the sire of the black horse Avatar in stable one, so Copenhagen's offspring is Influencer in stable two.

17.

Disraeli was second and didn't pull up last time, didn't refuse (that was Asquith) and didn't fall (that was the horse in fourth) so he must have unseated his rider and is trained by Moran. Asquith wasn't first, could not have been second and can't be fourth as he did not fall last time out so he finished third and is trained by Quinn. Baldwin was trained by North so Callaghan must be trained by Parkes. So Callaghan can't have pulled up last time so must have fallen last time out and now finished fourth. This means Baldwin pulled up last time out and this time was the winner, trained by North.

18.

The horse who finished sixth was not Oscar, could not have been Golf, Lima or Alfa (who was a length in front of a horse) so must be Sierra (who was fourth in the betting). Golf was two lengths behind the second favourite so must be ninth, with Lima in tenth. This also means that the second in the betting finished eighth. For a horse to finish a length behind Alfa, Alfa must be seventh, leaving Oscar to be eighth. Golf was not fourth or fifth in the betting, or second or the favourite, so he must have been third, with Alfa as favourite. And Lima was fifth in the betting.

19.

Cook's mount – drawn one – is not wearing cheekpieces and cannot be wearing a hood (Boyne's mount) or a noseband (drawn four) so must be wearing blinkers. Allen on Morgana can't be wearing blinkers, a hood or cheekpieces so must be wearing a noseband and drawn four. Drawn ten, Penelope can't be wearing blinkers (drawn one), cheekpieces (Nantucket) or a noseband (Morgana) so must be wearing a hood and be ridden by Boyne.

This means Driver's mount is Nantucket who is drawn eight and wears cheekpieces and Opal, drawn one, is ridden by Cook and wears blinkers.

20.

Athos's stable is one higher than the eight-year-old's, so the eight-year-old is not in stable four and Athos is not in stable one. As the seven-year-old is next to the nine-year-old, and the horse in stable two is aged six or eight, the seven-year-old and the nine-year-old can only be in stables three and four.

As the number of Athos's stable is one higher than the number of the eight-year-old's stable, Athos cannot be in stable four so Porthos is in stable four. Porthos is not the seven-year-old so must be the nine-year-old, and the seven-year-old is in stable three. As there is a horse in between Aramis and Athos, Athos must be in stable three, Aramis in stable one and D'Artagnan in stable two.

The eight-year-old is in stable two and Aramis is the six-year-old in stable one.

21.

The filly sired by Abacus is not trained by Matthews, cannot be trained by Nolan, nor by Osborne, so must be trained by Price. The colt who finished first cannot be trained by Matthews, Price or Nolan so must be the horse by Divide trained by Osborne. Therefore, Matthews must be the trainer of the mare. The runner sired by Calculus is not a mare so must be trained by Nolan. The second is not sired by Calculus so must be trained by Price.

The gelding must have finished third and the mare sired by Biometric is trained by Matthews.

22.

When Conqueror beat Triangulate by a nose, he was not 5-1, 3-1 or 2-1 so must have been 4-1. Out of Unicorn and Rivalry, one is beaten a short head when Conqueror was 2-1 and the other was second when Boyne rode at 5-1, so when Driver won by a neck, Steerforth must have been second. Unicorn was not beaten a head, so must have been beaten a short head, when Conqueror was 2-1.

So, Rivalry was beaten a head when Boyne rode Conqueror at 5-1. Unicorn wasn't second when Allen rode Conqueror, so Triangulate must have been second to Conqueror, ridden by Allen.

Therefore, Unicorn was beaten when Cook rode Conqueror and the winning distance was a short head.

23.

If Allen is always second, there are only six possible sequences in which the four jockeys can finish. In two of those, Driver would be the winner and he has so far only won once. So, Driver was first and Allen second. Cook has already finished fourth behind Driver, so must be third on this occasion, with Boyne in fourth.

24.

His win at Denley on good going was not in the third season, the fourth (Armfield) or the first (firm going), so must have been the second season.

His win at Cornham when third favourite was not in the first season, can't be second, can't be fourth, so must be third. When he won on soft, he was favourite, which can't be first, second or third so must have been in the fourth season. The going at Cornham must have been good to soft.

This means Goodtogo was fourth favourite on his second seasonal debut and second favourite for his win in the first season, which was at Bowminster.

25.

The horse who was unplaced last time out is not second, third or fourth so must have run in the first race. Therefore, the one who was fourth last time out must have run in the second race. As the one who was fourth last time out ran immediately before the race in which the horse was carried out, the horse who was carried out must be in the third race. The one who fell was second or third last time out so must be in the fourth race. For the horse who was second last time out to come immediately after the race in which one was pulled up, it must be the third race and the one who was pulled up must be in the second race.

So, the one who was third last time out must have been in the fourth race and it was the first race in which the trainer's horse unseated his rider.

26.

The winner could not have been drawn one, two, three or four so must have been drawn five, who was number three on the racecard. The best possible finish for number four on the racecard is third, so the horse drawn three must be fifth. Number one on the racecard must have finished fourth or fifth and number five must have finished fourth or fifth, so only number four, also fourth in the betting, can be third and also drawn one.

The only finishing place for the second in the betting, drawn four, can be second. To finish in front of number one, the third in the betting must have been fourth and be number five on the racecard.

So, the favourite was number one on the racecard and finished fifth.

27.

The sponsored race on Thursday was the mile and the sponsor was the brewery or the finance company. The bookmaker must have sponsored Saturday's race. The bookmaker can't have sponsored the mile or the sprint, so must have sponsored the two-mile race. So, the finance company must have sponsored the sprint on Friday. On Thursday the brewery sponsored the mile race.

28.

In the first race, Jamie's selection cannot have been first, second, third or fourth so must have been unplaced, at 5-4. The 6-4 shot who finished third in the one-mile handicap must have been in the fourth race. So, the horse who finished fourth must have been in the fifth race and the winner must have been in the second race.

The 10-1 runner in the two-year-old race can only have finished second, so the unplaced horse must have been in the two-mile race and the 8-1 horse must have been Jamie's winner in the second race.

29.

Land trained the horse finishing last home – Mercury – with Californium in fifth. If Argon finished in between Californium and Coulthwaite's horse, then Argon must have been fourth and Coulthwaite trained the third. Strontium cannot be second or first so must be third and must have Moore's horse and Murphy's horse on either side of him. The only way to have one trainer with the same number of letters as his horse is if Moore trains Argon and Murphy trains Neon to be second.

Anthony trained Californium and Blackwell trained Silver – the winner!

30.

When he carried 8st 10lb, it was not with cheekpieces, blinkers or a hood so it must have been with a visor. When he carried 8st 9lb he was not wearing cheekpieces, hood or a visor so must have been wearing blinkers. Therefore, he carried 8st 11lb with cheekpieces at Armfield. On his fourth outing, he cannot have carried 8st 9lb, 8st 10lb, or 8st 12lb, so it must have been 8st 11lb, at Armfield. He carried 8st 12lb before his run at Bowminster so he must have worn a hood at Cornham in his first race and carried 8st 10lb on his second run wearing a visor at Bowminster.

31.

The horse who finished first cannot be 3-1, 5-2, 5-1 or 7-4, so must be Pandemonium at 16-1. The best possible finish for Rousseau is third, so the 5-2 horse must be fifth. Titanium must be fourth or fifth and Sassafras must be fourth or fifth, so only Rousseau, ridden by Ashton, can be third, at 3-1. The only place that Carter could have ridden the 7-4 shot was second. To finish in front of Titanium, Dunphy must have been fourth, riding Sassafras. This leaves Earnshaw to finish fifth on Titanium.

32.

The 5-1 shot who won by a nose was not Swiss Roll or Spanish Armada and cannot be French Exit (short head) or Dutch Courage (2-1) so must have been Roman Holiday. The 4-1 half-length winner is not Swiss Roll so must be Spanish Armada. Dutch Courage did not win by a length so Swiss Roll must have won by a length and Dutch Courage must have won by five. The horse at evens cannot be French Exit who must have been 10-1.

So, the horse who won at evens must be Swiss Roll, winning by a length.

33.

The going was not soft in the fourth, third or second win (won by a neck, not two lengths) so must have been in the first, by two lengths, and can only have been sponsored by the brewery.

Heavy going was in the race sponsored by the bookmakers so good going must have been in the race sponsored by the finance company, which was the third race. Therefore the going was heavy in the second race, which was won by a neck, and sponsored by the bookmakers.

The five-length win must be in the third race, which means the winning margin of ten lengths must be in race four, sponsored by the TV channel.

34.

Allen cannot have been with Osborne (Driver was), Matthews, Nolan or Price so must be with Rawcliffe. Allen won it in the third or fourth year. So the jockey riding for Nolan won it in the fourth year or this year. And the jockey who rode for Matthews won in the second or third year. The first year's winner must have been trained by Price (Osborne didn't train it, Rawcliffe trained the winner in the third or fourth year, Nolan won it in the fourth or fifth year, Matthews in the second or third year), and it can only have been ridden by Boyne.

Eastwood did not ride Topaz, Lapis Lazuli, Morganite or Moonstone so must have ridden Sapphire. Eastwood did not ride for Price, Rawcliffe, Nolan or Osborne so must ride for Matthews, so Allen won the third running on a horse trained by Rawcliffe. So, the fourth running must have been won by Moonstone, trained by Nolan, and can only be ridden by Cook.

Allen won on Lapis Lazuli, and Driver won the most recent running on Topaz, trained by Osborne.

35.

The third horse (number one on the race card) must have been the colt, which means that number three was the gelding. Chicago was therefore the filly and finished second. The colt cannot be Chicago or Denver so must be Baltimore.

This means Denver must be the gelding.

36.

The maiden over seven furlongs is not the third race, cannot be the fourth race (handicap for three-year-olds and above) and cannot be the first race (six furlongs), so it must be the second race. The four-year-old handicap with 19 runners is not the first race, it can't be the second (the maiden) and it can't be the fourth (handicap for three-year-olds and above) so it must be the third. The mile race has 17 runners, so it cannot be the first, second or third race and must be the fourth (and the third race was five furlongs). This means there were 20 runners in the second race and 18 runners in the first race, which was the nursery.

37.

The each-way gambler who won a little didn't drink wine, tea or beer so must have been Jude the coffee drinker. The Trixie gambler and tea drinker didn't win most, couldn't have won a little, nor lost a lot as they didn't drink beer so must have lost a little and be Alex. Jamie must have had a Yankee so is not the wine drinker so must be the beer drinker who lost all their stake.

This means the Patent backer drinking wine is Chris, who won well.

38.

The winning jockey was not Ashton, and could not have been Bradshaw, Carter or Earnshaw (someone finished three behind Earnshaw), so must be Dunphy. Bradshaw was one behind the 24-year-old (not Dunphy) so must be fourth, with Carter fifth. That means that the 24-year-old finished third. Earnshaw must be second as he finished three in front of the next jockey, leaving Ashton to be third. Bradshaw was not one of the two oldest, nor the youngest or second youngest, so must be the 30-year-old, with Earnshaw, who must be next to Ashton, the youngest at 22.

Carter is the oldest at 36.

39.

As Harriet is opposite Adrian, she is not the woman who is the operations manager. Rachel is clerk of the course, so the only woman who can be operations manager is Lucy. As the operations manager has Adrian on her right and Samuel on her left, Samuel must be to the right of Harriet. So Samuel drinks black coffee. Rachel must be the woman on Adrian's right. The head of marketing must be on Rachel's right, meaning Harriet is the head of finance. For the tea drinker to be on the left of the catering manager, Adrian must be the catering manager and Lucy drinks tea. This means Samuel is the chief executive and Daniel, the head of marketing, drinks water.

40.

Neither Domingo, Alcatraz, Bravado or Caligula can have been last. Farrago must have been sixth, with Excess therefore third. If Bravado was at least two places in front of Domingo, he can't have been fourth. He was not first or third so he must have been second. As Caligula was at least two places in front of Alcatraz then he can only be first. As Caligula is one place in front of Bravado, then Alcatraz must be one place in front of Domingo and they must be fourth and fifth respectively.

TELL ME THE ANSWER AND I'LL TELL YOU THE QUESTION

1.
Which woman trained the Grand National winner in 2013?

Sue Smith with Auroras Encore

Venetia Williams trained the Grand National winner in 2009 with Mon Mome, and Lucinda Russell trained the Grand National winner in 2017 with One for Arthur.

2.
Which race named after a monarch was first run under that name in 1937?

King George VI Chase

The Queen Anne Stakes was first run under that name in 1930; the Queen Elizabeth II Stakes was first run under that name in 1955.

3.
Which runner-up in the 2,000 Guineas won the Irish 2,000 Guineas in his next race?

Kingman (2014)

Sir Percy (2006) won the Epsom Derby in his next race and Barney Roy (2017) was the last 2,000 Guineas runner-up to win the St James's Palace Stakes in his next race.

4.
Which two-time winner of the Champion Hurdle had his second win aged eight?

Comedy of Errors (1975)

Sea Pigeon was 11 when he won the Champion Hurdle a second time (1981) and Hurricane Fly was nine for his second win (2013). Hardy Eustace also won his second Champion Hurdle aged eight in 2015.

5.
Which 21st century Epsom Derby winner was the first to be sired by Cape Cross?

Sea the Stars

Galileo was the first 21st-century Epsom Derby winner to be sired by Sadler's Wells. Motivator was the first 21st-century Epsom Derby winner to be sired by Montjeu.

6.

Which former racecourse closed in 1970?

Alexandra Park

Hurst Park closed in 1962 and Manchester in 1963.

7.

Which jockey's autobiography was called *A Weight Off My Mind*?

Richard Hughes

Keiren Fallon's autobiography was called *Form* and Barry Geraghty's autobiography was called *True Colours*.

8.

Who trained their first St Leger winner in 2015?

Ralph Beckett (Simple Verse)

Roger Varian trained his first St Leger winner in 2014 (Kingston Hill) and Laura Mongan trained her first St Leger winner in 2016 (Harbour Law).

9.

Which two-time winner at the Cheltenham Festival had his first win there in 2010?

Sizing Europe, in the Arkle Challenge Trophy Chase

Simonsig had the first of his two Cheltenham Festival wins in 2012 in the Baring Bingham Novices' Hurdle and Hurricane Fly had the first of his two Cheltenham Festival wins, both Champion Hurdles, in 2011.

10.

Which winner of the King George VI and Queen Elizabeth Stakes ridden by Johnny Murtagh went on to win the Juddmonte International?

Duke of Marmalade (2008)

Novellist (2013) went on to win the Grosser Preis Von Baden. Dylan Thomas (2007) went on to win the Irish Champion Stakes and the Prix de l'Arc de Triomphe. Johnny Murtagh also rode Alamshar (2003) to win the King George VI and Queen Elizabeth Stakes but he did not win in his two subsequent races.

11.

What is the number of complete furlongs in the longest race traditionally run at Glorious Goodwood?

20 in the Goodwood Handicap of two miles, four furlongs and 134 yds

The number of complete furlongs in the longest race traditionally run at Royal Ascot is 21 in the Queen Alexandra Stakes of two miles, five furlongs and 143yds. The number of complete furlongs in the longest race traditionally run at Chester's May Festival is 18 in the Chester Cup of two miles, two furlongs and 140yds.

12.
Who trained their first 1,000 Guineas winner in 2004?

Mark Johnston with Attraction

Pam Sly trained her first 1,000 Guineas winner in 2006 with Speciosa. Aidan O'Brien trained his first 1,000 Guineas winner in 2005 with Virginia Waters.

13.
Which race named after a monarch was first run under that name in 1921?

Queen Mary Stakes

The King George Stakes was first run under that name in 1911 and the King Edward VII Stakes was first run under that name in 1926.

14.
Since 1970, which champion flat jockey had 11 years between his first and last championship?

Willie Carson (1972–83)

Pat Eddery had 22 years between his first and last championship (1974–96) and Kieren Fallon had six years between his first and last championship (1997–2003).

15.
Which race at Kempton, named after a winner of the King George VI Chase, is run over a distance of two miles, four and a half furlongs?

Silviniaco Conti Chase

The race at Kempton named after a winner of the King George VI Chase and run over a distance of three miles is the Kauto Star Novices' Chase. The Desert Orchid Chase is over two miles, as is the Wayward Lad Novices' Chase, also named after a winner of the King George VI Chase.

16.
Which Grand National winner of the 1990s was ridden by Nigel Hawke?

Seagram (1991)

Royal Athlete (1995) was ridden by Jason Titley and Tony Dobbin rode Lord Gyllene (1997).

17.

Which dual winner of the Chester Cup had their first win in 1999?

Rainbow High, whose second win was in 2001.

Top Cees won his first Chester Cup in 1995 and his second in 1997. Anak Pekan won his first Chester Cup in 2004 and his second in 2005.

18.

Which grey won the Ascot Chase in 1999?

Teeton Mill

The grey One Man won the race in 1998 and the grey Monet's Garden won the race in 2007 and 2010.

19.

Which Oaks winner ridden by Ryan Moore won the Pretty Polly Stakes on her next outing?

Minding (2016)

Love (2020) won the Yorkshire Oaks on her next outing. Snow Fairy (2010) won the Irish Oaks on her next outing.

20.

Which horse beat Take the Stand into second place to win the Cheltenham Gold Cup?

Kicking King (2005)

War of Attrition (2006) beat Hedgehunter into second place to win the Cheltenham Gold Cup. Best Mate (2002) beat Commanche Court into second place to win the Cheltenham Gold Cup.

21.

Which of the five racecourses in North Yorkshire is the southernmost?

York

Catterick is the westernmost racecourse in North Yorkshire. Redcar is the northernmost racecourse in North Yorkshire. The other two racecourses in North Yorkshire are Ripon and Thirsk.

22.

Fame and Glory started favourite for the Epsom Derby and finished second to which horse?

Sea the Stars (2009)

Hawk Wing started favourite for the Epsom Derby and finished second to High Chaparral (2002). US Army Ranger started favourite for the Epsom Derby and finished second to Harzand (2016).

23.

Which jockey rode his first 2,000 Guineas winner on a horse trained by Richard Hannon Snr?

Michael Kinane (Tirol 1990)

Johnny Murtagh rode his first 2,000 Guineas winner on Rock of Gibraltor (2002) trained by Aidan O'Brien. Both Kieren Fallon (King's Best 2000) and Walter Swinburn (Doyoun 1988) rode their first 2,000 Guineas winner on a horse trained by Michael Stoute.

24.

Which horse was the first six-year-old to win the Coronation Cup after 2000?

Warsaan (2004). He previously won as a five-year-old in 2003.

Mutafaweq (2001) was the first five-year-old to win the Coronation Cup after 2000. Boreal (2002) was the first four-year-old to win the Coronation Cup after 2000.

25.

Which race named after a royal residence was first run under that name in 1946?

The Royal Lodge Stakes

The Sandringham Stakes was first run under that name in 2002 and the St James's Palace Stakes was first run under that name in 1834.

26.

Which jockey rode the winner when Aidan O'Brien trained the first three in the Irish Derby in 2011?

Colm O'Donoghue (Treasure Beach)

Padraig Beggy rode the winner in 2019 (Sovereign) and Joseph O'Brien rode the winner in 2014 (Australia) when Aidan O'Brien trained the first three.

27.

Which five-year-old won the Tingle Creek Chase in 2005?

Kauto Star

Twist Magic won the Tingle Creek Chase as a five-year-old in 2007; Master Minded won the Tingle Creek Chase as a five-year-old in 2008.

28.

Which rider of back-to-back winners of the St Leger this century rode the second of those winners for trainer Jeremy Noseda?

Frankie Dettori (Sixties Icon 2006)

The first of Frankie Dettori's consecutive winners was Scorpion for Aidan O'Brien in 2005. Andrea Atzeni rode Kingston Hill for Roger Varian in 2014, followed by Simple Verse for Ralph Beckett in 2015. William Buick rode back-to-back winners, both for John Gosden, on Arctic Cosmos (2010) and Masked Marvel (2011). Ryan Moore also rode back-to-back St Leger winners in 2017 and 2018 on Capri and Kew Gardens, both for Aidan O'Brien.

29.

Which winner of the Gordon Stakes this century, who followed up with a win in the following season's King George VI and Queen Elizabeth Stakes, won the Ormonde Stakes in between?

Harbinger (2009 and 2010)

Highland Reel won the Hong Kong Vase and Secretariat Stakes in between winning the Gordon Stakes and the following season's King George VI and Queen Elizabeth Stakes (2015 and 2016). Conduit won the Breeders' Cup Turf in between winning the Gordon Stakes and the following season's King George VI and Queen Elizabeth Stakes (2008 and 2009).

30.

Which horse beat Kentucky Hyden into second place to win the Triumph Hurdle?

Tiger Roll (2014)

Peace And Co (2015) beat Top Notch into second place to win the Triumph Hurdle. Our Conor (2013) beat Far West into second place to win the Triumph Hurdle.

31.

Which novelist and former jockey wrote the novel *Taking the Fall*?

Tony McCoy

John Francome wrote the novel *False Start*, whilst *Dead Cert* (1962) was the first of many novels written by Dick Francis.

32.

Since 2001, which Grand National winner ran in the race the following year and finished fourth?

Monty's Pass, winner in 2003

Don't Push It, Grand National winner in 2010, ran in the race the following year and finished third. Mon Mome, Grand National winner in 2009, ran in the race the following year and fell.

33.

Which Prix de l'Arc de Triomphe winner was the first to be sired by Danehill?

Dylan Thomas (2007)

Found (2016) was the first Prix de l'Arc de Triomphe winner to be sired by Galileo. Treve (2013 and 2014) was the first Prix de l'Arc de Triomphe winner was to be sired by Motivator.

34.

Which Berkshire racecourse opened in the 19th century?

Windsor in 1866

Ascot opened in the 18th century, in 1711. Newbury opened in the 20th century, in 1905.

35.

Which jockey rode his first Eclipse Stakes winner on a horse trained by William Haggas?

Paul Hanagan (Mukhadram 2014)

Tom Queally rode his first Eclipse Stakes winner on a horse trained by Henry Cecil (Twice Over 2010). James Doyle rode his first Eclipse Stakes winner on a horse trained by Roger Charlton (Al Kazeem 2013).

36.

Which jockey rode Wayward Lad to the last of his three wins in the King George VI Chase in 1985?

Graham Bradley

John Francome rode Wayward Lad to the first of his three wins in the King George VI Chase in 1982 and Robert Earnshaw to the second of his three wins in the King George VI Chase in 1983.

37.

What is the number of complete furlongs in the cup race traditionally run at York's Ebor Festival?

16 in the Lonsdale Cup of two miles and 56 yards.

The British Champions Long Distance Cup on British Champions Day has 15 complete furlongs being run over one mile, seven furlongs and 209 yards. The number of complete furlongs in the cup race traditionally run at the St Leger Festival is 17 in the Doncaster Cup of two miles, one furlong and 197 yards.

38.

Who rode Relegate, trained by Willie Mullins, to victory in the Champion Bumper at Cheltenham?

Katie Walsh (2018)

Ruby Walsh rode Briar Hill, trained by Willie Mullins, to victory in the Champion Bumper at Cheltenham in 2013 and Patrick Mullins rode Champagne Fever, trained by Willie Mullins, to victory in the Champion Bumper at Cheltenham in 2012.

39.

Which jockey rode their only Epsom Derby winner in 1997?

Willie Ryan on Benny the Dip

Olivier Peslier rode his only Epsom Derby winner (to date) in 1998 on High-Rise. Michael Hills rode his only Epsom Derby winner in 1996 on Shaamit.

40.

Which horse was the first six-year-old to win the Arkle Challenge Trophy after 2000?

Azertyuiop (2003)

Well Chief (2004) was the first five-year-old to win the Arkle Challenge Trophy after 2000. Contraband (2005) was the first seven-year-old to win the Arkle Challenge Trophy after 2000.

TIME FOR A RHYME

1.

For many years racegoers were thrilled and beguiled

By the exploits of this offspring of **Flower Child**

His starts numbered 70, his wins 34

To win a great Gold Cup, he kept pulling out **more**

Desert Orchid

Desert Orchid was by Grey Mirage out of Flower Child. His sole victory in the Cheltenham Gold Cup came in 1989 when, after a memorable tussle with Yahoo, he got in front in the last 100 yards to win by a length and a half.

2.

Twenty-two hurdles races, 11 were won

Normal rider McCoy and trained by **Henderson**

His speed over a hurdle was a sight to see

In the green with yellow hoops of owner **JP**

Binocular

Binocular, owned by JP McManus, trained by Nicky Henderson and ridden by Tony McCoy, won the Champion Hurdle in 2010. He also won two Christmas Hurdles at Kempton.

3.

He beat Florida Pearl in the King George by ten

A fifth win in the race for his trainer **Doumen**

More wins were to come in Ireland and at Aintree

In the safe hands of the trainer's son **Thierry**

First Gold

First Gold was trained in France by François Doumen and ridden in most of his races by the trainer's son Thierry. He won the King George VI Chase at Kempton in 2000. His other wins included the Punchestown Gold Cup and the Martell Cognac Cup.

4.

Perhaps the best with which Greystoke was ever graced

His sire in both the Guineas and Derby was **placed**

At fences he was flamboyant, fast and clever

With his Champion Chase win one of the best **ever**

One Man

One Man was trained at Greystoke in Cumbria by Gordon W. Richards. His sire, Remainder Man, was second in the 2,000 Guineas and third in the Epsom Derby in 1978. His 20 wins included a Hennessy Cognac Gold Cup and two King George VI Chases. His last win was in the Queen Mother Champion Chase in 1998.

5.

He made the move to Newmarket as a young man

Coming from a top racing family in **Milan**

His multiple Group One wins are there to be seen

As is his daughter who shines on the TV **screen**

Luca Cumani

Luca Cumani's mother Elena was a champion amateur jockey and his father Sergio was a champion trainer. His daughter Francesca is a racing presenter on ITV.

6.

Over 2,000 winners for this baronet

In over 50 years at Heath House, **Newmarket**

He won two Champion Stakes with Alborada

And the Prix de l'Abbaye and Nunthorpe with **Marsha**

Sir Mark Prescott

Sir Mark Prescott took over the running of the yard at Heath House in 1970. He trained Alborada to win the Champion Stakes in 1998 and 1999. Marsha won the Prix de l'Abbaye de Longchamp in 2016 and the Nunthorpe Stakes in 2017.

7.

Two first season Group One wins was a super start

In 06, a second Middle Park with **Dutch Art**

A second season gave Guineas and Epsom glory

Then later a first Derby win for **Dettori**

Peter Chapple-Hyam

In his second season as a trainer, his Rodrigo de Triano won the 2,000 Guineas and Dr Devious won the Epsom Derby. They had, respectively, won the Middle Park Stakes and Dewhurst Stakes as two-year-olds. A second Epsom Derby win came in 2007 with Authorized, the first winner in the race for Frankie Dettori.

8.

He began in 14 with a successful year

From his stables based near Marlborough in **Wiltshire**

A 40-1 Guineas win left punters shook

And again four years later thanks to **Billesdon Brook**

Richard Hannon Jr.

Richard Hannon Jr. took over the training operation of his father Richard Hannon Sr. on 1 January 2014. His Night of Thunder won the 2014 2,000 Guineas at 40-1. In 2018 Billesdon Brook won the 1,000 Guineas at 66-1.

9.

Both Gosden and Godolphin recognised his spark

His father was a leading jockey in **Denmark**

He won the Derby in the silks of royal blue

Of 2020 jockeys he was number **two**

William Buick

William Buick rode his first Classic winner for John Gosden on Arctic Cosmos in the 2010 St Leger. Since 2015 he has been retained by Godolphin. He was born in Norway and his father Walter was champion jockey eight times in Denmark and once in Norway. He won the 2018 Epsom Derby for Godolphin on Masar and was second to Oisin Murphy in the 2020 jockeys' championship.

10.

On the flat and over jumps, winners aplenty

Entered the 2,000 club in **2020**

On the flying Battaash he wins top sprints with ease

Had an Eclipse win and Arc third on **Ulysses**

Jim Crowley

Jim Crowley switched to flat racing after a successful career as a jump jockey. He became the sixth current jockey to win 2,000 races in Britain, flat and jumps combined, when winning at Goodwood in August 2020. He has partnered Battaash in a number of top sprint wins and rode Ulysses to win the Eclipse Stakes and to third in the Prix de l'Arc de Triomphe in 2017.

11.

2,000 and 1,000 Guineas, he's won both
His first Derby win was in 99 on **Oath**
Two Arcs on Dylan Thomas and Hurricane Run
Now hopes his successes will be matched by his **son**

Kieren Fallon

Kieren Fallon rode five winners of the 2,000 Guineas and four of the 1,000 Guineas amongst his 16 English Classic wins. He won the Epsom Derby on Oath in 1999. He won the Prix de l'Arc de Triomphe on Hurricane Run in 2005 and on Dylan Thomas in 2007. His son Cieren won his first Group One on Oxted in the 2020 July Cup.

12.

His dad for Swindon Town was a football player
He captured the Gold Cup on a famous **stayer**
In the Guineas he beat Frankie by a short head
Now he has swapped the saddle for TV **instead**

Jason Weaver

Jason Weaver, whose father Eric played for Notts County, Swindon Town and Northampton Town, won the 1995 Ascot Gold Cup on Double Trigger. He won the 1994 2,000 Guineas on Mister Baileys by a short-head from Frankie Dettori on Grand Lodge. His TV work includes being a presenter and pundit for ITV Racing.

13.

The Dubai World Cup saw him achieve great glory
His jockey in nine out of ten was **Dettori**
In nine races, no doubt about the outcome
He lost only once, in the Derby at **Epsom**

Dubai Millennium

Dubai Millennium won nine of his ten races. His only defeat came in the 1999 Epsom Derby, when he finished ninth behind Oath. Following his impressive wins in 2000 in the Dubai World Cup and Prince of Wales's Stakes (the only race in which he was not ridden by Frankie Dettori), he was named best racehorse in the world for that year.

14.

At Newmarket in May she had a sparkling win

First 1,000 for the colours of **Godolphin**

As Epsom favourite she was nowhere to be seen

Eventually finishing nine of **15**

Cape Verdi

Cape Verdi won the 1998 1,000 Guineas for Godolphin, ridden by Frankie Dettori. She started 11-4 favourite for the Epsom Derby. In the race she was bumped and hampered and finished ninth behind High-Rise.

15.

Described by the monarch as one of her best stars

It was appropriate that she won the **Queen's Vase**

Then led one out and under strong pressure stayed on

To win the Gold Cup by a neck from **Simenon**

Estimate

Estimate, owned by Queen Elizabeth II, won the Queen's Vase at Royal Ascot in 2012 and the Ascot Gold Cup in 2013.

16.

Unplaced in the Guineas at 100-1

Later in 05 he was clearly **'Champion'**

Won first outing next year in Dubai Duty Free

Eclipse after that was Group One win number **three**

David Junior

David Junior, trained by Brian Meehan and ridden by Jamie Spencer, won the 2005 Champion Stakes at 25-1. He won the Dubai Duty Free Stakes in March 2006 and his third and final Group One win was in the Eclipse Stakes later that year with Notnowcato in second, who went on to win the race the following year.

David Junior started at 100-1 in the 2005 2,000 Guineas and finished 11th behind Footstepsinthesand.

17.

The first winner he trained was the last that he rode
Since then from Beechdown stables his winners have **flowed**
Speedy sprinters are still his speciality
But second Middle Park came with **Supremacy**

Clive Cox

Clive Cox trains at Beechdown Stables in Lambourn. Harry Angel, Profitable and Golden Horde are some of the top-class sprinters that he has trained. Supremacy won the 2020 Middle Park Stakes. Good for the Roses in a maiden Hurdle at Newton Abbot in 1991 was the first winner he trained and the last that he rode.

18.

With Henbit, Nashwan, Troy, three Derbys did he win
Six Legers too, one for the Queen with **Dunfermline**
His third St Leger win was with bold Bustino
The best he trained was beaten once, by **Roberto**

Dick Hern

Dick Hern began training in 1957; he was champion trainer four times and won 16 Classics in all. His best horse was Brigadier Gerard, beaten only once in 18 races by Roberto in the inaugural running of the Benson and Hedges Gold Cup, now known as the International Stakes.

19.

Thomas, Walsh, Fitzgerald rode his Gold Cup first three
An eighth King George came with **Silviniaco Conti**
His 12th King George win was in 20 with Frodon
He enjoys a win at local course **Wincanton**

Paul Nicholls

Paul Nicholls trained the first three in the 2008 Cheltenham Gold Cup – Denman, Kauto Star and Neptune Collonges, who were ridden, respectively, by Sam Thomas, Ruby Walsh and Mick Fitzgerald. He trains at Manor Farm Stables in Ditcheat, Somerset, about ten miles from Wincanton.

20.

From a quiet start as a trainer, he went far

And produced a National winner for **Freddie Starr**

He broke all the training records over the sticks

And even at Royal Ascot his wins numbered **six**

Martin Pipe

Martin Pipe trained the 1994 winner of the Grand National, Miinnehoma, owned by comedian Freddie Starr. He broke many records in his training career, being champion trainer 15 times and training over 4,000 winners.

21.

With Botti and Varian his talent he's honed

Winning Ascot's King George and QE on **Postponed**

Having arrived in England when just 17

He had won two St Legers by **2015**

Andrea Atzeni

Andrea Atzeni comes from Sardinia and his first work in England was for Marco Botti. In 2015 he won the King George VI and Queen Elizabeth Stakes on Postponed, trained at the time by Luca Cumani. He has ridden for Roger Varian and won consecutive St Legers in 2014 and 2015 on Kingston Hill and Simple Verse.

22.

Top rider for Hannons senior and junior

Won on seven out of eight one day at **Windsor**

Champion Hurdler Monksfield was ridden by dad

He won the Irish version riding **Cockney Lad**

Richard Hughes

Richard Hughes was champion jockey on the flat in 2012, 2013 and 2014 and has ridden a great deal for Richard Hannon Sr and Richard Hannon Jr. In October 2012 he rode seven winners from eight rides on one day at Windsor. His father Dessie Hughes won the Champion Hurdle on Monksfield in 1979 and Richard rode Cockney Lad to win the Irish Champion Hurdle in 1997.

23.

Won the Betfair by 11 on Agrapart

First in the Ultima on **Coo Star Sivola**

Into the record books when riding Tea for Two

In July 2020 time to say, **'Adieu'**

Lizzie Kelly

Lizzie Kelly won the Betfair Hurdle in 2015 on Agrapart and the Ultima Chase at the 2018 Cheltenham Festival on Coo Star Sivola. She was the first female jockey to win a Grade One race in Britain on Tea For Two in the Kauto Star Novices' Chase at Kempton Park on Boxing Day 2015. She retired as a jockey in July 2020.

24.

A first Grade One in the 2015 Challow

Another in the Clarence House aboard **First Flow**

Has ridden for Pauling, Bailey and Henderson

In the 16 National, beaten by only **one**

David Bass

David Bass won the Challow Hurdle on Barters Hill, trained by Ben Pauling, in 2015. He won the Clarence House Chase on First Flow, trained by Kim Bailey, in 2021. He began riding for Nicky Henderson when aged 21 in 2009. In 2016 he rode The Last Samuri for Kim Bailey to be second in the Grand National to Rule The World.

25.

He runs over five furlongs as quick as a flash

On three occasions he has won the **Epsom Dash**

By the second win at Epsom, he was seven

He still won races at the age of **11**

Caspian Prince

Caspian Prince has had over 20 wins from over 100 starts, including three in the Epsom 'Dash', in 2014, 2016 and 2017, the latest at 25-1.

26.

Second in the 2,000 and just five years on

One better place by Footstepsinthesand, his **son**

Five Group One wins in 12 weeks was a tour de force

And resulted in his nickname, **The Iron Horse**

Giant's Causeway

After finishing second in both the Newmarket and Irish 2,000 Guineas in the year 2000, Giant's Causeway won five consecutive Group Ones between 20 June and 9 September. The unbeaten Footstepsinthesand was one of his first offspring and won the 2005 Newmarket 2,000 Guineas.

27.

Second in the Leger under Pat Eddery

She had produced a sixth Oaks win for **Sir Henry**

Her sire Diesis, her dam Princess of Man

Her 'Generous' owner – **H.H.H. Prince Fahd Salman**

Ramruma

Ramruma's Oaks win in 1999 was trainer Henry Cecil's sixth. She was owned by H.H.H. Prince Fahd Salman, whose greatest success was with Generous, who won the Epsom Derby, King George VI and Queen Elizabeth Stakes, and the Irish Derby in 1991.

28.

Twice a neck second in the King George and QE

His only Group One win came under **Dettori**

Six lengths second in the Champion to Cracksman

His last race at York was a second to **Japan**

Crystal Ocean

Crystal Ocean was five times second in Group One races, including being twice beaten a neck in the King George VI and Queen Elizabeth Stakes, by stablemate Poets Word in 2018 and by Enable in 2019.

29.

He has runners on the flat and over the sticks

His magic gelding won the Chester Cup by **six**

He's won at each course from Perth to Newton Abbot

Frankel's son supplied a first win at **Royal Ascot**

Ian Williams

Ian Williams trains in Alvechurch, Worcestershire. His Magic Circle won the Chester Cup in 2018 and The Grand Visir was his first Royal Ascot winner in 2019. He has trained a winner at every racecourse in the UK.

30.

He is providing rides for his namesake and son

He achieved the ultimate double on **Dawn Run**

His horse won the Grand National for Tony McCoy

Two years later, was second with **Sunnyhillboy**

Jonjo O'Neill

Jonjo O'Neill as a jockey rode Dawn Run to win the Champion Hurdle in 1984 and the Cheltenham Gold Cup in 1986. He trained Don't Push It to win the 2010 Grand National, ridden by Tony McCoy, and in 2012 his Sunnyhillboy was beaten a nose by Neptune Collonges. Currently his son Jonjo O'Neill Jr. is enjoying success as a jockey.

31.

His first season as a trainer brought him much joy

Like a Cheltenham Festival win – **Burntoakboy**

But in 2014 he had his greatest day

When he won the National with **Pineau de Re**

Dr Richard Newland

Dr Richard Newland is a former general practitioner who trains in Worcestershire. He trained Burntoakboy to win the Coral Cup at the Cheltenham Festival in 2007 and Pineau de Re to win the Grand National in 2014.

32.

Son of a famous dad, with whom he shares his name

With Ballabriggs' National he too gained Aintree **fame**

Successive Fighting Fifths in ten and 11

All hurdles wins for Peddlers Cross equalled **seven**

Donald McCain Jr

Donald McCain Jr, son of Red Rum's trainer Donald McCain, trained Ballabriggs to win the 2011 Grand National. He also trained Peddlers Cross to win the Fighting Fifth Hurdle in 2010 and Overturn to win the race the following year. With Donald McCain Jr, Peddlers Cross won seven hurdle races including two Grade Ones.

33.

To be the champion soon is his greatest wish

To ride a winner, skipped an exam in **English**

The farmers' son from Somerset has shot to fame

Not least for wins on Politologue and **Cyrname**

Harry Cobden

Harry Cobden, whose parents are Somerset farmers Will and Sarah, skipped his English GCSE exam to ride a 33-1 winner at Leicester trained by Anthony Honeyball. In 2015-16 he joined the Paul Nicholls yard. His wins for Paul Nicholls include the 2017 Tingle Creek Chase on Politologue and the 2019 Ascot Chase on Cyrname.

34.

First to win the National and Cheltenham's big four

Nineteen hundred and twenty was his final **score**

He says since his teens he had been like a coiled spring

He won his first Gold Cup on Tom Taaffe's **Kicking King**

Barry Geraghty

Barry Geraghty became the first jockey to have won the big four races at the Cheltenham Festival – the Champion Hurdle (four times), the Queen Mother Champion Chase (five times), the Stayers' Hurdle (two times) and the Gold Cup (two times) – as well as the Grand National (on Monty's Pass in 2003). His first Cheltenham Gold Cup win was on Kicking King in 2005, trained by Tom Taaffe. He retired in 2020, having ridden 1,920 winners.

35.

From first rides in the 90s he was quick to learn

His first Champion Hurdle he won from **Overturn**

Won Cheltenham's Dawn Run on Willie Mullins's mare

And a second Champion Hurdle on **Buveur d'Air**

Noel Fehily

Noel Fehily won the Champion Hurdle in 2012 on Rock On Ruby, with Overturn in second, and in 2017 on Buveur d'Air. He won the Dawn Run Mares' Novices' Hurdle in 2019 on Eglantine Du Seuil, trained by Willie Mullins.

36.

A first professional win in 2002

Then three Irish champion titles he did **accrue**

To two Grand National wins Tiger Roll he did steer

And had two Festival wins on **Lord Windermere**

Davy Russell

Davy Russell had his first professional win as a jockey at Sedgefield in November 2002. He was Irish champion jump jockey in 2011-12, 2012-13 and 2017-18. He rode Tiger Roll to win the Grand National in 2018, when the combination was described as the oldest jockey (38) on the smallest horse (15.2 hands), and again in 2019. He twice rode Lord Windermere to win at the Cheltenham Festival, in the RSA Chase (2013) and the Cheltenham Gold Cup (2014).

37.

Ridden in nine Grade One wins by Paddy or Joe

With his superb jumping he could put on a **show**

Won the Champion Bumper at 40-1

A Betfair fourth, a second and three that he **won**

Cue Card

Cue Card won nine Grade Ones, including three Betfair Chases. His first Grade One win was in the Champion Bumper at the Cheltenham Festival in 2010. He was ridden in all of his wins by Paddy Brennan or Joe Tizzard.

38.

Noel Fehily was most often on board when he won

Thirty-six runs of which seven wins at **Grade One**

Two King George wins ensured his everlasting fame

At Kempton they have a steeplechase in his **name**

Silviniaco Conti

Silviniaco Conti won the King George VI Chase at Kempton in 2013 and 2014. The Silviniaco Conti Chase is a Grade Two race run over two miles, four and a half furlongs at Kempton Park in January.

39.

When aged 12 he came back to Leopardstown once more

And took his Hennessy Gold Cups total to **four**

At the Cheltenham Festival his wins were double

His Gold Cup best was second to **Looks Like Trouble**

Florida Pearl

Florida Pearl's wins included the King George VI Chase in 2001, the Martell Cup in 2002 and four Hennessy Cognac Gold Cups in Ireland in 1999, 2000, 2001 and 2004. At the Cheltenham Festival, he won the Champion Bumper in 1997 and the RSA Chase in 1998.

40.

The jockey, as so often, was Tony McCoy

For a Champion Hurdle success from **Macs Joy**

When aged 11 he made another headline

With an Irish Champion Hurdle win in **09**

Brave Inca

Brave Inca, trained by Colm Murphy and ridden by Tony McCoy, won the Champion Hurdle in 2006 by a length from Macs Joy. His many other wins included two Irish Champion Hurdles, the first in 2006 and the second, aged 11, in 2009.